The Accidental Spy

DAWN HANNA

D1603141

DORRANCE
PUBLISHING CO
EST. 1920
PITTSBURGH, PENNSYLVANIA 15238

The contents of this work, including, but not limited to, the accuracy of events, people, and places depicted; opinions expressed; permission to use previously published materials included; and any advice given or actions advocated are solely the responsibility of the author, who assumes all liability for said work and indemnifies the publisher against any claims stemming from publication of the work.

All Rights Reserved
Copyright © 2022 by Dawn Hanna

No part of this book may be reproduced or transmitted, downloaded, distributed, reverse engineered, or stored in or introduced into any information storage and retrieval system, in any form or by any means, including photocopying and recording, whether electronic or mechanical, now known or hereinafter invented without permission in writing from the publisher.

Dorrance Publishing Co
585 Alpha Drive
Pittsburgh, PA 15238
Visit our website at *www.dorrancebookstore.com*

ISBN: 978-1-6366-1269-0
eISBN: 978-1-6366-1855-5

Dedicated to my father, a man who freed thousands of political prisoners at the end of the Iraq War. Tragically, he could not free me.

Also dedicated to my mother and brothers, who fought for me every step of the way and did time along with me on the outside.

TABLE OF CONTENTS

Chapter Summaries

Chapter 1 : Farewell Flock: Mina Sallon (36) wakes up and discovers that the birds are gone. They've flown south somewhere for the winter and soon, she will, too (via automobile) since her name is now carved into a "no-fly list." Mina, a voluptuous and wealthy American woman (with Chaldean roots) has been convicted of violating a federal trade embargo with Iraq in 2003. Her brother Micah, the baby-faced genius, and Mina had owned a company called Curve Tech and she served as its top broker. Micah called Mina "the hammer." He would open the door and she would plow through it. She was the edge that took their business to the next level. But her greedy business acumen did not come without consequences. It's 2008 and she must relocate from the only home she's ever known, in Michigan, to a federal prison in Kentucky. She bids farewell to her family flock to serve her time.

Chapter 2 : Check in to Hell: Mina is used to calling the shots, but hell has a new king: the American prison system. The prison swallows Mina Sallon whole like a python constricting her. It takes away her identity, strip searches her, and assigns her to sleep in "the bus stop," which is aptly named as inmates and guards pour in and out of it like a Greyhound depot. The open space housing 100+ women vaporizes any ounce of what's left of Mina's privacy and entitlement. She forms an unconventional friendship with her bunkmate, Miss Briana (Miss B), a poor African American woman with a Jesus obsession and a strong liking for prison. Mr. Clark, a former military officer, is her counselor. He explains the ins and outs of the prison system. Long-standing prisoner Miss Kelly, a white, Machiavelli-type antagonist, is also in attendance at the counseling session. Mina forms a mundane routine: sleep, eat, yard time, repeat.

Chapter 3 : Everyone on My Goddamn Case: Mina flashes back to her arrest, the U.S. Immigration and Customs Enforcement team aim straight for the jugular. They charge and arraign Mina and Micah with Conspiracy to

Break the United States Trade Embargo with Iraq, Money Laundering, and Making False Statements. Mina flashes to her sentencing where a jury of her "peers" passes judgment upon her. The jury is comprised of mostly small-town, rural people with short attention spans and a proclivity toward racism. The prosecution is successful at confusing the jury by carving and re-carving the definition of the crime, presenting hundreds of hours of case detail, and painting Mina as a terrorist. Prosecutor Quinn MacCann (otherwise known as *She*) states that Mina "may have placed the whole country at peril." Both MacCann and Judge Battaglia make an example of Mina. The gavel slams down: Guilty. Noise follows: Traitor! Terrorist! Treason! Conspiring with Saddam Hussain! Un-American!

Chapter 4 : More Than a Visitation: Inmates ready themselves for visitation like it is prom: They extract their cleanest Kentucky State emerald greens, brush their hair, and paint their faces. It is Mina's first visitation, and she is expecting her entire family to attend. It turns out to be much more than simply a visit. First, her father doesn't show up. He can't free his daughter, so he decides that his calling is to free political prisoners in Iraq. What's more, Mina loses her appeal, although her family keeps this a secret from her. Also, Mina's mother slides her some cash (which is the start of a lucrative side hustle) even though possession of it can cause Mina serious consequences.

Chapter 5 : Mina "The Other": Mina experiences racial profiling at a level she's never seen. It begins when an African American clique stares daggers in her direction, like she has some sort of fatwa on her head. An inmate says, "There are two reasons people stare in prison. They want to hurt you, or they want to take something from you." Soon, Mina realizes that she, in fact, is being targeted. An inmate spills details regarding her case (particularly with respect to her supposed treason) and the outcome transitions into full-blown violence. Sadly, Mina also learns that she's lost her appeal, which spirals her down into an even darker rabbit hole.

Chapter 6 : A Field Guide to Surviving Prison: There are distinct rules in federal prison that cons must abide by to avoid being punted "behind the fence." Behind the fence means a maximum-security prison with stricter rules, fewer privileges and greater punishments. However, Mina soon realizes that her survival ultimately depends on the bending of said rules, transitioning her into a woman who commits petty crimes, including but not limited to the

Bribery of an Employee, the *Possession of Money*, and the *Possession of Stolen Property* (including 25 carrots). Miss B and Mina also start a business enterprise that focuses on importing hard-to-obtain goods for cash or commissary. Their measly $50 a month wage won't cut it.

Chapter 7 : A Field Guide to Surviving Prison II: *Disobeying Direct Orders, Destroying Property,* and *Creating a Disturbance* all contribute to Mina ending up with an Incident Report that Mr. Clark writes. Miss Kelly orchestrates the whole confrontation without getting her hands dirty. She enjoys toying with Mina as a form of amusement. Mr. Clark gives Mina some solid advice. "Mind your damn business. Don't disrespect anybody. Do your time. And don't feed the animals; they'll associate you with food." Miss Kelly is just that, an animal, and Mina isn't going to feed into her bullshit anymore.

Chapter 8 : Open Season: Mina's stock value is at an all-time high with the inmates. Her new nickname is "The Robin Hood of Kentucky." Cons respect her and her generosity. The business Miss B and Mina have created is now a well-oiled machine, complete with a new employee, Charlie, who is now in charge of daily operations. Sadly, the success of their business places an even greater target on Mina's back. And when a drop (full of black-market items, including a letter from Mina's mother) goes missing and ends up in the hands of a snake, Mina is forced into a compromising position.

Chapter 9 : Venomous Spiders: When Mina and Miss B receive a supper summons from Miss Kelly, they feel duty-bound to oblige. After all, Miss Kelly holds evidence that can land Mina's mother in prison. The dinner is held in a creepy location, Devil's Den, where experiments were conducted on insane patients long ago. After all, this Kentucky Prison is built on a former insane asylum. And the experience of eating in this room sends Mina onto her back, literally, and into Medical. On top of being poisoned, she develops MRSA. Miss B swings back at Miss Kelly with a vengeance and is shipped behind the fence into a maximum-security prison.

Chapter 10 : No More Visitors: Besides Miss B's prompt departure, Mina learns that her mother has had a stroke and won't be visiting anymore. Mina is cut off from everything that matters to her. She is sent to The Green Mile with the bad cons and 24/7 fluorescent lights overhead because "prison is by association." Since Mina is an associate of Miss B's, she is also pinned for Miss Kelly's severe beating. Mina develops vertigo to add to her never-ending list of ailments. She also has dark thoughts. She writes, "As I curl up in my very public bunk, I think a lot about death. How some people slip into it, via pills or an overdose, and how others are shot with it, via a Colt 22. Or how some people – like Saddam – hang in the air until their voice box collapses." Miss Kelly offers her a dark solution to her woes: suicide. Just when Mina is on the verge of giving up, she learns of her release date. She's getting out for "good behavior."

Chapter 1

Farewell Flock

I woke up and discovered that the birds had gone. A drop in temperature accompanied the silence. Something about quietness chilled my bones. I was an extrovert, a bold, unfiltered, and – drum roll – newly convicted Chaldean woman. The wintry discomfort never left my body after the sentencing. My ribs felt like icicles, like they could shatter at any moment. Then my body would fold in half and I'd fall to the floor. Thump. A gavel slammed down: Guilty. Then noise followed. I was a traitor, a terrorist, I'd committed treason, I had conspired with Saddam Hussein, I was un-American. Followed by utter, uncomfortable and stinging silence.

It was November 2008, the month and year I made this tardy discovery. All of the wings in Michigan had flown to Florida, or Georgia, or wherever snow-birds flew. How could one really tell? It may have dawned on me because I was placed on a no-fly list. Or, because I was migrating south myself (via automobile) and nothing at the time seemed chirpy. Or perhaps it was because I had never paid attention to the little things before. I wasn't skilled at being present. Either way, I wouldn't wake up again in Michigan, the only home that I'd ever known, for a long time. I'd rise to the pestering sound and shit of Kentucky fowl. I was headed to prison, soon-to-be caged, prodded and plucked.

*   *   *

We were in a lone Durango on a long road. A gray overcast sky made the day even more austere. I couldn't stop sighing. I knew it was driving my brother nuts, but I didn't care. Micah, sweet, baby-faced Micah who was acquitted of the charges for which I was found guilty. We ran a business together, once. He was the brain, the golden egg. He taught a college-level engineering course when he was 19 and earned a PhD in his 20s. I suppose I was the edge he needed to take our company Curve Tech to the next level. After all, I was the hammer, as he called me. He would open the door and I would drive through it. Boom! But that was before we were arrested. Before we lost it all. Before the hammer cracked the egg and our company poured out into a skillet, scrambled.

Micah cut through the quiet. "*She* can't kill *us* anymore. It's over."

She was the prosecutor. Micah thought she had a personal vendetta against me. That *She* made an example of the half-Iraqi woman. *She* became a U.S. attorney on the heels of my conviction. Was it a coincidence or a stepping-stone? I didn't know at the time. Either way, Americans hated Arabs, especially after 9/11. But I wasn't Arab. I was American. My father was born in Iraq but had been an American citizen since before I was born. Neither Micah nor I had ever been to Iraq. We didn't even speak Chaldean or Arabic.

"Hello, are you listening?" Micah insisted. "I said, she can't kill *us* anymore."

"Yeah, I'm listening." My mind was always drifting. My brother called it zoning out. It generally made people feel like I wasn't listening. I was headed to prison… it was hard to focus.

Us, I thought. *Us?* For a moment I clung to the word because I knew it wouldn't last. Micah was grouping me with him. He tried to make me feel like he was part of my prison sentence, to reaffirm the impression that I was still in the family nest. After my sentencing, my family was afraid to say anything to me. They were scared their words would send me flying off a cliff. I get it. It was over. The trial, the late submission of evidence that would acquit me, the appeal (spoiler alert: I lost). But *my* life was over. I was 36 and I'd be missing the best part of it.

Okay, I had already been to Greece nine times, I had a closet full of cashmere, and moisturized with La Mer. Cue applause. But I worked my ass off. I traveled as an international broker for Curve Tech, and structured meeting after meeting after meeting. I bulldozed through impossible deals. And I took a lot of crap, from a lot of different personalities, in a lot of different countries. I deserved all that I had.

I collected a little nest egg for a rainy day (well, a big one… hush, hush). The money was gone now. Lawyers charged up the (insert derogatory word). And what was it all for? I couldn't stop thinking that I'd never be able to cultivate a family, a husband, kids, and a golden retriever named Liberty. It was all knocked back into dreamland.

My eggs were on the verge of evaporating, my mother's worst nightmare (respectable Chaldean women were to be married off before the age of 23 and produce lots of children). She was most likely at home writing another senator regarding the injustice of my case, which became her second job next to trying to save a slice of our company by changing the name. (It worked for Netflix.) But saying goodbye to me in a different state wasn't something she could face. What mother could? I was to call her when I got settled. I pressed my cheek to the cold SUV's window.

Earlier, I had been saying goodbye to my marble bathtub at three in the morning, while Chopin's violin played a defeated tune. It was now the bank's marble bathtub and the bank's condo, although it had been built with my prosperity. A cigarette lay smoked beside the tub and ash lined the tile. I held my breath underwater as my hair floated outward like tentacles reaching for the side of the tub. I wanted to see how long I could take it. A bubble escaped my nostril, then another. It was soothing in a way only people with small hope felt, I imagined, testing the lungs until I couldn't anymore.

Now, I was on an unfamiliar southern road, bordered with brittle birch trees, with fast food bags crinkled under my designer boots. It wasn't too late for me to jump from the car. I fantasized about popping open the door and rolling into the ditch. Or, I could have raced into oncoming traffic. A truck would do me in, I thought. There were still a couple hours left. It wasn't too late. It wasn't too late. It might kill my mother. But it wasn't too late. Our SUV zipped past the skinny branches – black – white – black – white – black. The leaves had fallen, and the trees looked emaciated. Or maybe I was starved. Micah packed all of my favorite comfort foods, which I had already shoveled down like some gluttonous spree en route to purgatory. I binge-ate when I was nervous. There was Faygo root beer, Ruffles chips, veggies with hummus, and Pacha (cow intestines stuffed with rice and meat). I thought the familiar food would bring back normalcy, but I barely tasted anything. Nevertheless, it was a perfect American/Chaldean mix. Bravo, Micah. Micah paid attention to detail. I didn't.

I hadn't even noticed that it was raining until my father, Mansur, adjusted the windshield wipers to full blast. His hands were gripped tightly on the steering wheel. His eyes surveyed me through the cloudy mirror, so much so that he didn't notice a truck merging onto the highway. The truck honked and he switched lanes like it hadn't even happened. My head lurched and hit the side window.

"You okay?"

"What?"

"You okay? Are you okay?"

"I'm fine," I said. "I'm fine."

I wondered if my dad's pulse even quickened. If it did, no one would have noticed. He was a proud, Iraqi man. And he didn't believe in sticking with the cards one was dealt, even if it caused a head-on collision. He had risen from an immigrant (who barely spoke English) venturing to America with $17 in his pocket, to a liquor store owner and a multi-millionaire. Later, he became a well-respected interpreter for the U.S. armed forces. He fled Iraq shortly after Saddam Hussein's Ba'ath party told him he had to join in the late 1970s. He fought hard to take down Hussain for Iraq and for America. But that wasn't enough. His kids had to be exemplary, too. He had high standards for others as well as himself. My father said things like, "Don't complain. Work harder," and "Blame yourself for your disappointments."

His sullen stare made me feel like I was being driven to my own execution. He was ashamed of me. I knew it. His daughter was going to prison. The daughter he once bragged about and favored, the daughter who once shadowed his every move.

I watched my father conduct business day-by-day, month-by-month, and year-by-year. Our nickname for him had always been "The Merchant of Michigan." The neon sign outside of his business flashed liquor and lotto and drew in a smorgasbord of people. Our clientele was predominately African American or others who were down on their luck, sauntering in barefoot from the trailer park next door, paying mostly in food stamps. His store was in a rough neighborhood of Mt. Clemens, Mich. Nonetheless, the shop was small, clean and stocked to the brim with goods. Even sandwiches were on the menu. There was something for everybody. Buy low and sell high was engrained in my mind at a young age. Also, the notion that all customers were to be treated the same way. "The business helps them, and they help us," my father said. It was a circle of success.

In middle school, I started selling hard-to-obtain goods procured through my father's business. My locker became my warehouse. I was slinging candy before it hit the market (promotional stuff that had been sent to my father). I'd sell it at school, between classes (at a price spike), even though I obtained the sugary gold for free. It was all profit. Cha-ching! I kept my earnings in a Wonder Woman lunch box.

I worked at the store making sandwiches from time to time. My father had a difference of opinion regarding the amount of deli meat that should go on each sandwich. My sandwiches were jammed with overflowing ham. His sandwiches wouldn't mollify a mouse. We fought constantly. When my mother asked how I was doing at the store, he answered, "She puts too much meat on the sandwiches."

My mother said, "She's a generous soul. What a beautiful trait." My mother always defended women, especially those who worked hard.

I graduated from selling candy and over-stuffing sandwiches to peddling hard-to-acquire items in high school. The 1980s were alive with punk rock, neon, feathered hair, the moonwalk and crotch grabs. My cousin sold me an original photo of Michael Jackson for $20. I promptly photocopied the shit out of it and turned the investment into $500. Oh, the way money made me feel!

I had a taste for buying and selling. It was inherited from my father, who always said that we should grow where we were planted. That I did. I watched him transmute alcohol into gold like an alchemist. We had a big house, designer clothes on our backs and money in our pockets. Funny enough, it was the early jobs (overseen by my father) that planted the brokerage skills that would ultimately land me in the federal prison to which I was en route. Go figure.

The GPS sounded, "Turn left onto Lexington Road/US-25 South."

Micah spoke up. "Does anyone need to use the restroom?"

Would this be the last time I'd hear his voice? No, there were still around ten miles left. Not yet. Not yet. The car seemed suffocating, like there wasn't enough air to go around. My breaths were short, and my hands were clammy. There was too much silence. Why wasn't anyone talking? I needed some white noise. It would make me feel better, I thought.

I unrolled the window, hung my hand out, and allowed the rain to plow my fingertips. The windshield wipers whirred back and forth. I dug my other hand into the last bag of chips. Maybe I'd taste something.

*   *   *

Little did I know that I wouldn't taste much for nearly five years. That's because the main food group for America's incarcerated was carcinogens. Prisons feed its felons cancerous cells on a plastic plate with a spork.

My best friend inside, Miss Briana (Miss B), developed kidney cancer as a result of being inside. Southern women I met there liked to put "Miss" before their names. It was a way of demanding respect. Miss B was in her mid-40s. She was African American and overweight, with false teeth and a penchant for headscarves. Granted, she didn't always eat the best food. She hailed from a low socio-economic group and organic wasn't exactly in her vocabulary. Hell, fruit wasn't in her vocabulary. Her uniform was always dirty with some sort of prison mash-up (make-shift pizza in the microwave or a potato log).

She carted a burgundy Bible around and quoted liberally from it. She thought that the Word of God might save her from the Kentucky prison we were locked up in, as well as the cancer that overtook her body and turned her urine black.

But, as my counselor Mr. Clark once told me as he cleaned his dirt-specked glasses, "Stick a fork in it; it's done." I hated him. Who did he think he was? Mr. Clark was also African American and a former military officer with a quiet command. He was smart, sarcastic, witty and tremendously annoying. The kind of annoying that played the fiddle with my insides. The first time I visited his office, I wanted to throw up the remnants of the beef stroganoff my mother made the night before so that I could still taste home in my mouth. And I wanted to aim the vomit toward Mr. Clark's smug face.

*   *   *

My mother, Ella, had planned a bon voyage party. By "party," I mean that we sat around her mammoth-sized dining table at a distance and picked at the beef stroganoff that she had over-cooked. Don't get me wrong. She was an extremely hardworking Irish woman, but any semblance of affection was sucked out of her the day before I went to prison. Bitterness for America had taken over her system. Have you ever tasted food peppered with hate and bitterness?

My mother, my brother Micah, and my father were all in attendance for my swan song. We scraped forks across green plates, pushed aside food and over-poured wine. The TV was on mute. The news flashed on the screen: severe thunderstorms were sweeping across Tennessee, Arkansas, Alabama and Kentucky. Kentucky was now a part of tornado alley. Perfect.

My mother readjusted her round glasses and stared at me in the dim light, eyes glassy. Her glasses remained sloped. Her right ear was higher than her left and I couldn't take my focus off them.

"You're in charge of your own prison. Remember that," she said.

"Is that a bumper sticker?" I replied.

Micah reached for my hand as a way of soothing my sarcasm. I exchanged his hand for more wine and chugged it.

"Sorry, Mom, I don't know what's wrong with me."

"Nothing is wrong with you. There is something terribly wrong with this country."

I saw Micah searching for something; something unreachable.

"If this is the worst thing that happens to us before forty, we're lucky."

Are *we?*

He must have felt like Judas that evening. He was my business partner. Yet, I was the only one going to prison. The genius was spared. My mom must have eaten a ton of avocado when she was pregnant with him.

An image of me popped up on the TV screen. There I was in that infamous photo. It had been taken for an avant-garde photo shoot my college friend talked me into. Now it haunted me. I wore a low-cut, black top. I was turned to the side with my hands resting on my lower back. My face was shadowed like some film noir star and the mole on my jawline was the focal point. When my image was projected across Michigan newsreels and articles, I understood that the media liked turning their targets into saints or pariahs. My dad cranked up the volume.

A news anchor spoke. "A Rochester Hills woman, Mina Sallon, was convicted by a jury of selling tech to Saddam Hussein, a violation of the 2003 federal trade embargo. Her brother and business partner was acquitted."

"I help fight Saddam and this is what they do to my kids," my dad said as he smashed his hand on the table.

"Turn it off, for God's sake, Mansur. Turn it off." He waved her away as he always did. She huffed as she always did.

Chaldean men ruled the roost, but my mother also ruled (which was the cause of their divorce when we were kids).

She grabbed the remote and changed it to Animal Planet, her go-to channel. Something about coming face-to-face with dangerous animals was on. A cougar was stalking a hiker.

My eyes couldn't stray from my mom's tilted glasses. I couldn't stop thinking that she'd need some sort of surgery to level out her ears. She couldn't spend her life off balance. I also couldn't stop thinking that tomorrow I'd be elsewhere.

"You can't go, you just can't," my mother said as she wiped her eyes.

"I'm not going to prison, mom. It's really more of a resort. There's an Olympic-sized swimming pool and a five-star chef."

I shoveled the well-done beef into my sarcastic mouth, closing it.

"You'll be out by Christmas if it's the last thing I do," my father said. "I can't have a piece of me in prison" He swiped the remote and clicked off the TV and, with a heartbeat, I was gone. Back to Mr. Clark's office.

When I first entered his office, it felt like there was a balloon inflating my chest. All I could emit were short breaths, as if my lungs were folded in half and I simply had to breathe in sharply to unfurl them. I couldn't gather enough strength to breathe deeply, though.

Mr. Clark's office was corporate and colored beige with a tiny triangular window (in which inmates in emerald green uniforms peered). There were no pictures or personal items. Just a plaque nailed to the wall boasting, "20 years of government service."

"I'm not supposed to be here," I said while my hands flailed. I could feel the blood flow to my cheeks and felt like an oven. My eyes watered.

Mr. Clark looked weary but still had some spark.

"Nobody is supposed to be here," he replied with heated sarcasm. "Stick a fork in it; it's done."

"Well done? I don't know, my lawyers are on it and they aren't cheap."

He reached for my glasses to wipe off the residue, as if the shiny new perspective would give me some clarity. I thought, why would I ever want a clear view into my new setting? The beige walls, the green prison uniforms that merged all inmates into one stream of toxic algae, and the deep-set wrinkles that held disrespect and menace? I preferred my rose-colored glasses.

But Mr. Clark was right on. *Stick a fork in it. It's done.* The cancer Miss Briana developed had spread its way to other organs. It's done. And the six years I'd have to spend in prison was just getting started. My fancy lawyers couldn't help me. The steak I'd cooked up was well done. In fact, it was burned to a crisp.

Chapter 2

Check in to Hell

I was used to calling the shots in life and in business, but hell had a new king who, in this case, was perched behind plexiglass. A guard, a steely man in his 40s (with a brain to match) called me up to the window and exchanged my Michigan license with a numbered identification: 30810-039. The year, 2008, was also printed on my new ID.

He said, "039's come from Michigan. Remember that."

Why the hell would I need to remember that 039's come from Michigan?

When I careened into a processing cell, it was the first time in my life that I had ever felt delicate and powerless. The prison swallowed me vacuum-sealed and whole. It stripped the outside air from my lungs. Its smell was complicated and invasive. The mold had crept in with humidity, but it was also mixed with bleach, $5 microwave dinners, toilets and rot.

I had read online that this specific prison used to be an insane asylum built in the 1800s. That explained the tiny windows at the top of each door. I imagined that it still drove people up the wall and into the barbed wire.

The processing cell was a minimalist's dream: one sink, one concrete bench and heat that could murder a cactus. My thick black locks stuck to my face. I remember hoping that I could get a good acne moisturizer in prison; probably not. I could feel the sweat saturate my olive complexion as I peeked through a fogged window. The outer prison grounds had rolling fields of yellow-stained grass. I drew an "X" on the window. Mina was here.

My rear end parked on the concrete bench, but I fidgeted. How long would was this ordeal going to take? I touched my silk blouse. The softness didn't go with concrete and corrections. It was the final touch of freedom. My hands shook. I gripped them together to stop the tremors. Too much coffee I thought. Yes, too much coffee.

Rachel, a former military guard with an impeccable uniform (and something to prove), opened the cell door.

"You're up, princess."

Rachel escorted me into an administration room. It was just as intimate, just as bland and just as hot. A dated, gray filing cabinet, a fake plant, and a scratched-up desk blended into the institutionalized heaviness.

Rachel took my fingerprints one by one. I stared at my ring finger, the white circle left on it and the last imprint of my fiancé. I didn't trust myself to think about him without falling into an even darker pit.

She slammed paperwork in front of me. It was personal information that I had to fill out. Like they didn't know who I was already. The government ... I swear to God.

Name: Mina Sallon, **Date of Birth:** December 2, 1972 (36), **Marital Status:** Formerly Engaged, **Weight:** 150 lbs., **Height:** 5′5″, **Hair Color:** Black, **Eye Color:** Brown **Education Level:** Master's degree, **Ethnicity:** I didn't know what to fill out for this; still don't... **Religion:** Christian.

Rachel pointed at my diamond cross around my neck. It had been a baptismal present from my grandmother. "Your mere existence gave her life," my mother always said. "She loved and believed in you." The diamond was two carats with clarity like glass, a VVS1 (very slightly included). There were no inclusions to the naked eye. Just like my sorry ass before I was arrested.

"Hand that over for inspection," she said.

I passed it over with reservation. She inspected it clumsily. Sentimental tokens had no place in prison. She held it up. It sparkled in the fluorescent lighting.

"Surrender it, or I ship the rock."

The diamond was popped out with a paperclip. Rachel sized it up.

"I think I'll buy a nice, rare steak with this puppy."

"Bitch," I said, in Chaldean. One of the few words I knew.

She smiled and popped it into a bag. She said, "I fought in Iraq, you know. Learned a few words. A few other things, too."

Rachel carted half of my paperwork into another room. I eyed it as remnants of my makeup and my character left the room without me. A paper shredder sounded. I didn't know then what I know now. The bitch shredded my master's degree.

And I never saw that diamond again.

Back to business: Rachel escorted me next door. The room was bordered with prison essentials: uniforms, shoes and soap. I met Rachel 2 (another loser with something to prove). However, she had about 10 years on Rachel, plus greasy hair and a bleached mustache. She brought me a bra, underwear, a top, pants and shoes … all beige. She set the "comfort items" on a desk, out of reach.

The reflective windows caged me in. There was nowhere to hide.

Rachel 2 was mechanical about her movements, like she had been working in prison for a good part of a sad, sad life. I still heard the paper shredder in the neighboring room, buzzing away like it had a life of its own. More of a life than I had now. Buzz, buzz, buzz.

Rachel 2 asked, "Anything to declare?"

I shook my head, no. Buzz, buzz, buzz.

"Any sharp objects in places they shouldn't be?"

I shook my head, no. Buzz, buzz, buzz.

"Any tattoos or unusual markings?"

I shook my head, no. Buzz, buzz, buzz.

"Take off your clothes."

"Can I leave my underwear on?" I asked.

She shook her head, no. Buzz, buzz, buzz.

I felt small and sheepish. I covered my breasts and kept my eyes on the slow-moving fan above me as it cast shadows on my skin, whoosh, whoosh, whoosh.

"Hands at your sides."

I uncovered my breasts and held my breath. I rubbed my sweaty hands on my thighs. But my hands wouldn't stop crying. Buzz, buzz, buzz.

"Squat and cough." Squat and cough? I wondered what the inmates smuggled in: drugs, money, weapons? I later learned that smuggling in what's called "contraband" equaled more time. When would this be over?

Not yet. She ran her rough hands through my black hair as I grimaced. I hated being touched. A light flashed in my mouth.

"Lift up your tongue." Buzz, buzz, buzz.

She flashed the light into my eyes. I blinked.

Bureau of Prisons Health Services, 2008	Inmate Name: Sallon, Mina Description	Reg # 30810-039 Type
Health Problem 11/30/08	ADHD *we do not medicate	Chronic
Health Problem 11/30/08	Common migraine	Chronic
Health Problem 11/30/08	Shoulder Pain	Acute

*   *   *

The hallway, which a white inmate with red eyes named Blaze led me down, was stripped of all color and character. It narrowed with every step, like I was entering the body of a python. I wasn't happy to shed everything connected with my former life. My job, my family, my fiancé. I was squeezed deeper into the extraordinary world (with the other new mice) and stood out in a forest of green. All of the veteran inmates wore emerald green. They looked eerily similar. All the new girls wore beige. One newbie couldn't stop crying. I felt like punching her. She was making it ten times worse. We carted necessities: hygiene items and an itchy, gray bedroll.

The felons gathered by race: Blacks, Whites, Hispanics and Others. Catcalls, taunts and heckles echoed down the tube-like passageway. A group of three Black women whipped an orange back and forth. The alpha con (an Amazon named Trina) catapulted it at me. It smacked me straight in the cheekbone:

"What the fuck!" They laughed. I didn't.

"What is she, a Mexican?"

Clearly, I was an "Other." That didn't bother me, since I quickly surmised I'd been raised in a higher socio-economic group than well over 90% of them. Most of these women seemed uneducated, greasy and primal, like they had drifted out of some urban underground to hunt for cheese. The thought of cheese took me back to carnitas I once had in Miami with slow roasted pork that came apart like butter and melted black-truffle Manchego. Wow, what I would have given for one or two in that moment. Thinking about good food (which I did often in prison) made me feel like I wasn't supposed to be there. I wasn't supposed to be there. I wasn't supposed to be there. I was there. And I was grouped in with these women.

*   *   *

The bus stop, where I originally slept, was aptly named because inmates and guards poured in and out of it like a Greyhound station. It held 57 bunk beds, all lined up perfectly and packed to the rafters with felons. In contrast to the tangle of bodies, I noticed that federal prison was neat: beds were made, shoes were lined up, and personal items were tucked away. Blaze pointed to a top bunk in the corner, parallel to the stairwell.

"Mexican got a corner spot, pfffttt! Why don't you look me in the eyes when you fuck me," she said.

That was prime real estate. A tiny bunk bed in a packed, communal bunker with the overwhelming smell of cheap hair products hanging in the air.

Miss B sprawled out on the bottom bunk. She popped jellybeans into her mouth, adjusted her false teeth with her tongue in between chewing, and ignored me. She looked like Aunt Jemima. She had ice in Ziploc bags under her armpits. At first, I thought she had razor burn. Later, I realized she was hot. In November.

I knew Miss B had come from poverty because of the crusted stains on her emerald uniform, if one could call it a uniform. All other inmates wore crew shoes, but she wore boots as old as I was. I made the educated guess that she couldn't afford new kicks and I was right. She was heavily engrossed in a burgundy Bible. I read somewhere that inmates who were addicts in their real lives became addicted to Jesus in prison. It was the only thing that made them feel good for free.

It sounds silly, but I didn't know how to jump up on my bunk. I had never had a bunk bed before, and I didn't want to look spoiled or naive in front of this hodgepodge of low-income, streetwise women. I had never ridden a bus as an adult. I had rolled up my change and took it to the bank. I always had my own car with heated seats. Sue me. If I couldn't hop up, they would have assumed I was used to luxury. I always had my own room, my own space. I couldn't begin to explain or understand how I felt in that moment. It felt like a final stop. The final stop on a bus I'd fallen asleep on that had made its way to the depot. The moment held a kind of permanence. But at the same time, I was still on a smelly bus with wheels.

My eyes scanned around the bus stop, left to right, left to right. I saw a wild-eyed black woman, her focus pinned on me. She munched on a red apple. I later found out that her name was Ruth.

Miss B highlighted a passage in her good book, and I wondered what it was that deserved to be a main feature. Why was God punishing me? Why me?

Time slowed around me as multiple inmates circled our bunk. I didn't know what to do, so I stood there like one of those silver-painted mimes on the corner at an intersection begging for change. Somehow, they were owed money because of their unmoving talent.

I felt pinpricks in my chest, and I couldn't catch my breath. THIS is where I was going to sleep? I would be sleeping on this cot, with 100 eyes lurking all around me. I imagined that sleeping with cons would be a constant irritant to a normal mind.

I began to cry. Okay, I bawled and bawled and bawled. Couldn't help it. My tears fell uncontrollably. Great. Now they'd *really* think I was *really* spoiled.

Without warning, three black inmates rushed to my side and presented me with gifts that were supposed to calm me down (including a chair, which someone had stolen from my bunk as a joke). They also supplied me with ramen, sandals and Honey Nut something or other. The only thing that would have calmed me down in that moment was Peruvian ceviche (the best was from Miami) and my mom. They tried. They even made up my bed for me with the itchy bedroll. Nothing stopped my tears.

Miss B sighed. She was bothered by the kerfuffle. She kept sucking on jellybeans, the noise amplified with every chomp. She sighed again. It irked me. The last thing I needed was a grumpy bunkmate. Ruth rushed me and broke the silence:

"Don't cry. Have an apple. I'm Ruth. Ruth from Philly."

She handed me a half-eaten apple, one step away from crazy town.

I said, "I don't eat recycled food."

"You a shot caller, ain't ya?"

She spoke, finally. Miss B tapped on her bed. The three Black inmates left the scene and I thanked them with a nod.

"What's your name, baby?"

"Mina Sallon."

Ruth intervened, "Sallon, ah, are you a virgin?"

"I'm Miss Briana. Miss B." She coupled her words with an offered bruised banana that I didn't have the balls to turn down. Some people had the world and gave someone in need a penny. Others had a sole banana and handed it over.

"Where are you from?"

"Rochester Hills," I said. "Detroit."

"Lesson one: Don't say shit about anybody in here. Got it, Detroit?"

"I'm getting an appeal."

"I've been waitin' on mine for two years."

Ruth charged in again. "That why you still in your boots, ready to run or something, Miss B?"

Miss B stared coldly at Ruth, enough to make her step backwards.

"This isn't a bad place. Really nice, Detroit, really nice." Miss B stretched back in her bunk and rested a hand behind her head. Her eyes rolled back. She looked like she was on her way to a heavenly massage at the Four Seasons while sipping one of those 10-ingredient, chartreuse-green Bellinis. Her lips smacked together while she continued her jellybean binge.

Was she on crack? How could this woman possibly think that being in prison was living it up?

"We need to go to the short line," Ruth said, snapping me out of my judgmental trance.

*   *   *

The cafeteria was drained of life with muted green walls and a military-style setup. It seemed like those in charge wanted to get the inmates in and out as fast as possible. The emerald-clad inmates moved through the line mechanically, as if a puppeteer strung them along.

A tray smacked the countertop, stir-fry was plopped on, an inmate pushed forward. A tray smacked the countertop, stir-fry was plopped on, an inmate pushed forward. A tray smacked the countertop, stir-fry was plopped on, an inmate pushed forward. It was a production line. A zoo.

We scooted past a mural of trees and jungle animals. It was one of those paintings that committed every artistic sin known to man, both childlike and chilling.

"This is the early dinner for the diabetics and, well, anyone with problems," Ruth said.

"Doesn't everyone have problems?" I replied.

"Yes, silly, but these ones have *big* ones." She stressed the word big like the people in line had some form of the bubonic plague.

The stir-fry (or pile of brown mush with one carrot) hit my plate with force. They certainly had a cynical idea of what constituted food. Ruth shoved me.

"Onward," she said, "I'm starved."

We sat at a long table with the diabetics and the people with problems. Ruth shoved the questionable mush into her mouth with great enthusiasm. I poked mine. This was going to be a long six years. I was going to starve. Shit, I was going to starve!

In my periphery, a Black inmate stalked the microwave like a hyena while two lesbian inmates chatted intimately beside it. Lesbian 1 stroked the braids of Lesbian 2 suggestively. I could feel my hands sweat as my eyes drifted back to my "dinner."

I breathed short breaths and tried to focus on the tasteless brown chow. Just shovel it in, I thought. Don't draw attention to yourself. Ruth held up her spork (half spoon, half fork) as if to say, "This is it." This was it. I later learned that stir-fry was one of the better meals. Hilarious.

The microwave rang. The Black inmate sprung it open and grabbed the warm biscuit hungrily. Stole the biscuit, rather, from the lesbians. She took off with the bounty as if it were filet mignon. My heart beat rapidly as I watched them like animals in their natural habitat. The lesbians took off after the thief like lions. I half expected Morgan Freeman to chime in and narrate over the loudspeaker: "Every day creates an impossible journey in an environment so extreme that no one comes out unscathed."

I followed the chase, over tables, under tables and across the jungle mural. Other inmates knocked their trays on the tables egging on the hunt. My heart mimicked the drum of dishes. The cons hooted, hollered and howled. It was a scene straight out of *Lord of the Flies*.

The Black inmate crammed the bread into her mouth in one shot! She choked, but it didn't halt her movement. My heart felt like a parrot was attempting to escape between my ribs. Were there no guards for diabetics? What was the dinner for normal people like? Who the fuck was in charge? I wiped my paws on my beige uniform.

The lesbians tackled the Black inmate and took her to the floor, tenderizing her face like meat. My eyes were pinned on the attack. The Black inmate spat out the biscuit. With it came a bloody tooth and blood spatter. Two corrections officers ripped the lions off of their battered prey.

"Lions and tigers and bears, oh my," Ruth shouted.

"It's the hole for you," one officer grunted. The hole was just as it sounded: a dark and gloomy dungeon where "bad cons" were sent for breaking rules (including hunger-strikes). It was there that isolation reached its crescendo. As if an inmate wasn't already alone in prison. Surrounded by people, but still completely alone.

Twenty or so watches beeped synchronously, straight out of a horror film. It was 4 p.m.

*   *   *

"Count time! On your bunks! Be visible to staff," Rachel shouted. Her shoulders were upright, and she looked down on the cons as if her face was on a $100 bill. There was nothing worse than an idiot in a position of power. She held a tally counter. I will always remember the sound of being counted like cattle: click, click, click. It continues to be a constant nightmare.

Miss B repositioned me in front of my bunk so that I wouldn't receive an infraction. Thank you, Miss B, I owe you, I thought. Rachel stared me down. Her eyes shot daggers my way every chance she got. She wanted to punish me. Instead, she counted me, equally as dehumanizing: click. Mina 1, Rachel 0. I sensed it would be an ongoing feud.

"Clear," Rachel said.

The whole stance reminded me of the first day of my sentencing at the federal courthouse in Detroit.

*   *   *

USA VS MINA SALLON — DETROIT, MI — APRIL 2007 — 4:25 PM

We stood in place on low-pile blue carpet, or was it green carpet? No, it was blue, I think. Judge Peg Battaglia, a no-nonsense, senior judge with a plump face entered the court. Perhaps I raised my chin to see her. Yes, I must have. I wanted to view her head-on. The woman who would be in charge of directing the remainder of my life. In my mind, I could still see her walking to her raised pulpit with her stiff robe and stack of files. All eyes looked up at her.

Prosecutor Quinn MacCann (*She*) was watching. She carried an air of masculinity with her strait-laced bob and no-makeup face. Will Washington, her insipid assistant, flanked her. He whispered something into her ear, and she nodded. He looked to be in his 60s; he had about 20 years on her. I never heard a peep come out of Mr. Washington's mouth. He must have been silent for the entire sentencing, apart from his soft secrets.

"Why am I here," I may have said to my lawyer, Loren Monday. He smoothed his white hair and handlebar mustache.

"You won't be here long," he must have replied, confidently, in the way most New York criminal lawyers do. "Don't show any emotion." He had a first-class rating and won nine out of 10 cases.

When I dreamed of my sentencing, I always knew the verdict before the gavel pounded the bench. In the recurring dream, we all stood knee-deep in murky water. My father said our family would never drown. But my mother always fell into the dark cesspool. It wasn't a huge or small splash. What stood out is that no one turned around or helped her. My neck wouldn't move. I knew it was my mother because of her wail, low and guttural, much like the real event. And much like the real event, everyone continued to face the judge when Mom made that sound, the one that haunts me and sends shivers up my back. It felt like D-Day. My chest was empty, and my organs all poured out into the deep.

The dream had the adherence of concrete. Not wet concrete on my skin that easily wiped off. The kind of concrete that seeped into my veins and hardened. Whenever I snapped out of the dream, the stiffness stayed with me for a good part of the day.

My mother, my father and Micah stood still as the bailiff said something straight out of every criminal law playbook. Perhaps I held my breath.

"United States District Court for the Eastern District of Michigan is now in session. The honorable Peg Battaglia is presiding. You may be seated." A court reporter with round glasses locked the words into her typewriter.

All parties were on their best behavior, like obedient dogs. Most of the jury looked like it came straight out of a trailer park. Many were white with bad or outdated hair styles, wearing rumpled clothing. These were my peers? During jury selection, one potential juror got herself excused when she looked straight at me and told the lawyers that she knew in her heart I was guilty. Just by looking at me. Before any testimony was presented.

I knew in my gut the outcome wouldn't be good. My lawyer thought otherwise.

She responded with, "Good afternoon, your honor. Quinn MacCann and Will Washington on behalf of the United States."

I stared at the American flag (which appeared to ripple) in a room that was too quiet and too proper with its protocol and charades. I thought, if these two were *for* the United States, did that mean that I was automatically against it?

It's odd, but I can't recall sitting down. Did I thump down, or did I sit down softly? Perhaps I waited until everyone else sat. Was I standing for five minutes? More? Less? If I sat down last, it would have showed that I respected the judge the most. Yes, I must have done that. I must have sat down last.

*   *   *

After standing incessantly for authority figures a year earlier, I now sat in front of another, Mr. Clark. His office was the official place for inquiries, questions and complaints. There were sometimes guests in his office during counseling sessions. I gathered quickly that the inmates were eager to speak with him, were mostly manageable and flirted constantly, like he held the key to the city. He told me later that the longer I was there, the better he'd look. I doubted that. He spoke to me like an older man would. He was preoccupied with his own life and advice rolled out of him like it had been rehearsed a million times. It probably was.

"Prison is by association, so don't associate."

In one of our first sessions, there was a white inmate in her 60s in attendance. Why he allowed it, I'd never know. It seemed pretty rude. She had short, white hair with patches of baldness. Every so often, she tugged on what was left of her thin hair, a foul and most likely painful habit. Her name was Miss Kelly and I later learned she was a long-standing resident. She was crocheting something yellow. Was she foreshadowing something cautionary? Or maybe she was simply crafting a hat to conceal her head trauma. Still, I wondered if she was weaving more than hats in her web.

The gist of this meet and greet was to underline the ins and outs my new lodgings. Mr. Clark informed me that there would be an orientation in two weeks and that I'd be required to get a job and show up before I was allowed visitors. Basically, I'd be in here without contact from the outside world for 14 days. I thought I'd either die or faint, right then and there. I wanted to hug my mom, my earth angel, the woman who has always fought for me. I wanted to curl up with her. If I concentrated really hard, I could smell her. Vanilla and cinnamon swirls of her house and skin. She had a difficult life. She endured a horrendous divorce and had already lost both of her parents. She also lost her second husband of 21 years to cancer, just one year after he retired. And now her daughter was sealed tightly in a federal prison. My mother endured loss after loss after loss. My heart ached for her more than myself.

"Why is this happening to me?" I asked.

"*Why not you?*" Mr. Clark retorted. How sensitive, I thought.

Mr. Clark's news got worse. The GED program was mandatory, even though I had earned a master's degree. My advanced degree was misplaced from my file or (cough, cough) shredded by Rachel. Another loss. I told him that I wanted to file a complaint, which he called a grievance. He said that it would probably take longer than the completion of the GED program. It figured.

Mr. Clark nudged the readied box of Kleenex forward. I took a few sheets, mopped up my tears and blew my nose.

"First time in the clinker?" Miss Kelly offered.

I responded coarsely, "No, it's my 10th." It seemed like my answer piqued her interest. My father would have apologized for my outburst at that moment. He would have told her to pay no mind, and that I was both bold and childlike.

"Being alone doesn't really work in prison," she responded. "Better change that sarcastic tune fast or you'll be playing the violin without strings."

So, I'd be playing some sort of drum? I wondered.

Mr. Clark handed me a cup of coffee and I thought I'd start crying again. There was something about cupping a warm mug that made things feel better, until I sipped the coffee. I must have glowered. Miss Kelly continued with her own inquisition.

"What was your expertise, your degree?" She worked the yarn with calculation. "I bet it was business and that you owe restitution. Over a mill, I'd say." I realized Miss Kelly was the type of person that set traps with her cross-examinations into which cons would ultimately fall. She knew everything about everyone and didn't hesitate when she used their information against them for her own gain.

"Thank you for the coffee," was all I wanted to expose. But the nosey parker was right on. I did owe money to the government: $1.1 million, to be exact. The thought made my insides knot. So did she.

"Can I call my mom?" I asked Mr. Clark, who opened my file and looked intently for the first time. He wove through it with care.

"No calls," he said with disapproval wrinkling the corners of his mouth. "Let me give you a bit of advice. In here, we have the haves and the have-nots. The 'haves' must work harder to keep clean hands. Got it?" Miss Kelly nodded in agreement. Her opinion seemed to matter to Mr. Clark.

"So, because I have some means, I'll be punished in here with the other animals?"

"That's not what I said."

Another trap sprung, "What type of means?" Miss Kelly asked. Mr. Clark didn't correct her invasiveness. He may have been wondering himself.

"Money to buy snacks," I said curtly as I pulled a red herring out of my back pocket, continuing, "And what if I get sick?"

"Here's how medical works. If you're sick, take a Tylenol. If you're really sick, take an extra strength Tylenol."

I had ADHD but didn't want to ask him about stimulants in front of Miss Kelly.

"So, keep my hands clean. Got it."

Mr. Clark gave me a quick look. "Don't make a song and dance about it," he sniffed.

"Because health is minor in the scope of things."

He replied, "How many sarcastic pills did you pop this morning?"

I guess I was trying to show off, in the sense that I could snap back at any of his comments with ease. He was witty. I thought that the narcissist within him must have liked witty people. I didn't want to appear too showy. I wanted him to like me so that he'd give me a break. As usual, I went too far.

He pushed the phone forward and asked what my mother's number was. I knew he wasn't supposed to allow a phone call and I was grateful. My mother cried and I relayed that I'd see her in two weeks. She told me that the lawyers were saying by Christmas. I'd be out by Christmas.

About three new lawyers made the promise that I'd be out to sing, "I'll Be Home for Christmas," *if* my family provided enough cash. Lawyer No. 1 said that cases like this were hard to untangle, but that he'd do it for $100,000. Lawyer No. 2 said something similar. The government distorted and dumped information at the trial, but that he'd unravel it for $200,000. Lawyer No. 3 said the prosecution carved and re-carved the definition of the crime in an effort to confuse the jury. But that she could get me out for a large fee as well. Nonetheless, they all agreed on one thing. All it would take was one lawyer. One lawyer and I'd be released.

All it would take was one lawyer and I'd be released.

At the time, I didn't realize that the phone call home meant I owed Mr. Clark a favor. The morality code around here was heavily tilted. Navigating through the new flock, learning a new, twisted code and deciphering how to survive in hell would be rough. It was something to look forward to on a daily basis.

When I got out of prison (and trust me when I say I left with very dirty hands), and when Mr. Clark and I finally respected each other, he told me that he initially thought that I was a "spoiled rich mess." That some officers (who he refused to name) told him to pay attention to me. That I was a "mover and a shaker," a person who influences people and the actions of said people. It was easy to look up my case. The proceedings were all over the Internet. Interestingly enough, the intricate details were sealed. It was all very fishy.

Chapter 3

Everyone on My Goddamn Case

We were arrested two years earlier in July. The authorities really made a show of it. Blue and red lights flashing through the windows of Curve Tech. The lights danced across my suit as I made my way to what looked like a military SWAT team. They were, in fact, the U.S. Customs and Immigration Enforcement team and they were going for the jugular. I walked toward 10 or so men in suits with an arrest warrant and my handcuffed brother. Employees dodged my eyeline as I inched through the hallway. My throat constricted. I could not swallow.

I passed my mother at her desk. She was crying. When she spoke about what was going through her head later on, she said, "I never knew the government could be so twisted."

The top gun, Agent Ward (with hostile eyebrows), waved me forward. It felt like everything was in slow motion. I passed a yellow note to an employee, Brenda, which read, "Call lawyer."

Agent Ward handcuffed me and delivered his spiel. "You have the right to remain silent…"

Micah said, "We're not guilty."

My original thought (when they arrested us) was that we hadn't paid enough in taxes. Maybe our tax guy had miscalculated something.

Micah had related that his original thought was that a brokering client in London (Sami Al-Mufti), a middleman who had purchased some equipment from us in 2002, was a terrorist.

*   *   *

Sami Al-Mufti is a name I'll never forget. The Iraqi (with the thick accent) flew me to London in an effort to procure used telecommunications equipment from Curve Tech. Queen Elizabeth's mother had just passed away and the burial brought out a lot of somber faces. It rained heavily. We met at a Turkish coffee shop and smoked up a storm. It was a one-story building that was cylindrical in shape. The streets were busy with West London traffic and double-decker buses.

We sat inside, underneath a heap of hanging Turkish lamps and evil-eye trinkets. It was nothing fancy, but they took their coffee seriously there. It was served in tiny, ornate gold cups. Their heat felt good in my hands in the damp weather. The spicy cardamom scent was rich. There were mostly men in the shop, smoking and sipping from miniature cups. It was a typical Middle Eastern coffee culture. But no bother. I had always been comfortable in the presence of men. Sami called coffee houses "the schools of the wise," since so many deals were struck in them. He was happy to discover that I was a hardworking American girl, in his words.

When I verified that I could gather the items he wanted for pennies on the dollar, he shook his finger at me and said that we needed quality mobile switching centers and a quality third-party monitoring software program. He also stressed that the project would have a "positive impact on the USA." That it would make us "millions." I believed him.

"I see you like St. John," he said, in a way that seemed like an apology. Did he think I should have worn something better? A crocodile Birkin bag, perhaps? Now that I have marinated in this comment a million times, I assume that he was trying to make me feel inferior, which took my pride for a little ride. Perhaps his remark made me want that million-dollar deal a little more.

Nothing substantial stood out about Sami, other than the fact that he was posh and private. I asked him if he was married with kids, to which he replied, "Are we here for business or personal matters?"

Apart from that, he was a diligent coffee drinker and very generous. I did not pay one pound while in London. I also remember that whatever I asked him seemed to astonish him, like I was questioning his business acumen.

"What will the equipment be used for?"

He said, "What won't it be used for?"

I gulped the residual coffee grounds left in my gold cup and thought that was the end of it. We shook hands. It was an easy and lucrative deal. Or so I thought.

*   *   *

Two SUV doors slammed shut and my brother and I were driven away. They separated us. Soon enough, we were paraded (independently) through a federal building among whispers of, "Got them," like we had been sniffed out from some remote location. Meanwhile, both my brother and I could be found smack in the middle of Rochester Hills, Michigan. I was at Curve Tech most days, and Micah was either holed up at Dunkin Donuts, at Curve Tech, or teaching, researching or engrossed in lab work at a nearby university. I kept thinking that they had arraigned the wrong people and that they'd be terribly embarrassed.

I barely remembered the interview process that followed our arrest. I still don't. I could recount little links of what transpired, but not enough to form a whole event or a whole picture. My brother was somewhere close to the room I was in, I imagined, but out of sight and out of reach.

During the course of the long interview (conducted by the Bureau of Investigation and Customs Enforcement, the Department of Commerce, and the Federal Bureau of Investigations), I could hear my own loud voice as it twanged and echoed in the small, airless room. I could also remember the door as it clicked open and shut. Officials kept pouring in and out. They all seemed to blend together with their forgettable faces and gray suits. I sweated like a pig but only because it was July, and I didn't understand what they thought they had.

There was a lot of back and forth with respect to Sami Al-Mufti.

I said, "Sami Al-Mufti was the owner of a company called Leading Integral Electronics or LIE."

"Have you worked with him in the past?"

"Yes. I've helped him facilitate sales since 2002."

I remembered that the agents were particularly interested in a company called Projection Inc., a business out of Texas that sold global navigational equipment. I assisted in a sale between Projection Inc. and Leading Integral Electronics.

They asked, "Were you aware that the email return address of Projection Inc.'s was linked to Sami Al-Mufti's email?"

"No, I was not aware." I thought, what in the hell? Weird. Why had Sami's email been attached to Projection Inc.? I had always spoken with the president, a man named Ambrose Tiller.

The onslaught of their questions then focused on the destination of a package Sami had ordered (communications equipment) and where I thought the export was destined. I related that, to my knowledge, Sami was the "end user" in our most recent deal destined for Turkey. Sami would end up using the Global Positioning Systems, the used telecommunications equipment, the monitoring software program and related technologies. Sami told me he was setting up a new network there with a partner, Mr. Mehmet Yilmaz. I expressed, reiterated and echoed that, to my knowledge, the equipment was destined for Turkey. Again, again and again.

I provided proof. I received an email with a letterhead stamped with Leading Integral Electronics. In the email, the procured equipment had a clear target: Istanbul, Turkey (which Sami had forwarded to my email). This ended up being a billing address.

ATTN: Mr. Mehmet Yilmaz
High-tech and Development Inc.
Cankurtaran Mah. Yeni Akbiyik Cad.
Apt. 555 71151
Istanbul, Turkey

"Did you know that Iran, Afghanistan and Iraq were not permitted to receive exports from the United States in 2003?"

"Yes," I responded, "yes." Why was that relevant?

When I read the indictment, I didn't understand what it all meant. At times, I truly questioned if it was all a sick joke. The charges: conspiracy to break the United States trade embargo with Iraq, money laundering, and making false statements.

*   *   *

USA VS MINA SALLON — DETROIT, MI — APRIL 2007 — 5:45 PM

The sentencing was dramatic. While the trial had lasted more than two weeks, it didn't take long for the jury to form their decision. It seemed like minutes, which was odd, considering the scope of what everyone believed my punishment should be. The government was going for 20 years behind bars and my lawyer was saying probation.

It seems as if there were some kind of bugs in my chest. They weren't butterflies. Locusts maybe; a plague of locusts. Their wings crackled as they buzzed around and crashed into each other. It felt like my heart banged outside of my ribcage to make room for the pests. I couldn't concentrate. What did I have for breakfast? I know I had coffee. My stomach hurt. I'm fairly certain I looked up at the judge. I must have fixated on her, and I'm sure I tried to do it with as little emotion as possible, as my lawyer requested. I don't believe she connected with my eyeline. No, I don't think she did. Shit, this was bad. Did it mean she thought I was guilty? I recall that everyone's faces were stone-like, including those of my parents and Micah.

She broke my thoughts. "This was a very serious offense, and Mina Sallon did willfully undermine the embargo with this country. And at this time there were heightened tensions with Iraq because of the imminent war. We need to make it clear that the United States enforces its embargos and that the courts punish offenders when they violate embargos." And then she turned to me. "You may have placed the whole country at peril."

I may have placed the whole country at peril? This comment seemed more than far-fetched. Turns out, the tech equipment that Curve Tech sent to Sami Al Mufti would have been used to spy on Saddam Hussain and his henchmen had it not been discovered. It was sent to Iraq. It was not destined for Turkey. I didn't know it, but I was aiding in taking down a dictator, criminal and tyrant. I was an accidental spy, so to speak. Why was the U.S. punishing me?

Judge Battaglia responded with, "Miss Sallon, your sentencing guidelines are dramatic, do you understand?"

"Yes," I said.

"That these guidelines recommend a minimum of 15 years?"

"Yes," I said, holding my breath.

"Do you have anything to say before the court passes sentence?"

I wanted to say fuck you. Fuck the government for using me as a scape-goat in some elaborate scheme. I wanted to hand over a big "fuck you" to the prosecutor for concocting a false narrative. I wanted to send my middle fingers flying into the faces of the ignorant jury. And I wanted to say, "fuck you" to the judge for not seeing past it all. But I didn't. It wasn't in my character to be combative. There were times to stick my neck out. This wasn't one of them.

Instead, my response was: "When I read the government's memorandum, I don't recognize the person that they're describing. I did cut corners and I am sorry for that. I'm 36. I hoped to get married and have children, like everyone else. It is, however, hard for me to understand how such a severe punishment that the government is asking for is fair for my actions. Nonetheless, I am sorry for the bad judgment that I engaged in. I do take responsibility for that. I have let down myself and I have let down my family."

I wish I could have tidied up this scene and packed it away, in a box, in the back of my closet with my winter clothes. Instead, I exchanged my St. John boots for ten-dollar prison shoes.

*   *   *

I circled the track in my no-name crew shoes, like a gerbil wheeling itself to nowhere. I had not been there a week before it felt as if my former life had dropped away. I admit that I wasn't feeling my best. But some vitamin D would do me good, I thought. I walked under an overcast sky. Sigh.

I walked and walked and walked by a poorly constructed garden that made me hungrier every time I looped around it. I wondered how I'd be able to get my hands on the produce. I could see that they had grown carrots and cucumbers and corn, maybe? I unpeeled the banana Miss B had given me (which had transitioned from bruised to black) and took a bite. It would have been better in banana bread. I chucked it. It was biodegradable, right?

I walked and walked and walked around about 100 cons as they exercised in the open yard on parched, dying grass. Fight-or-flight responses were on high alert, heads whipped back and forth, and eyes were popped open.

Miss Kelly's watchful eyes were stationed in a pavilion. The *Wall Street Journal* flanked her, which Miss B later called "an expensive piece of paper." That always made me laugh.

Miss Kelly seemed to be politicking with her pets as she observed the yard. She sat on the very top of a picnic table: the highest point. In my father's words, she didn't take a back seat to anybody. She stroked the hair of Blaze, the young woman with the attitude who had showed me my bunk the first day.

There weren't fences at this federal prison. An inmate could presumably walk straight off the property if she could successfully dodge a stream of bullets and bum a ride to Mexico. I wondered what the best avenue out of here would be. I scanned the property. There were guard towers (manned by corrections officers) with rifles perched in the windows, there were cameras, and there was an exit gate wide open with trust.

"Hey baby, why don't you shake that ass over my way?"

Sure, yeah, that sounded like a banner time, shaking my ass for a random perp. Surprise: A men's prison was right next door. The men were closed in with a large fence hedged with barbed wire, a dramatic effort to shut out noise from the outside world.

I understood later that cons at the women's prison wanted to remain here. The smart individuals were exemplary inmates (or tried to be) and most called it "a camp." Hilarious. If one was transferred "behind the fence," it meant that they had broken a serious rule. Behind the fence meant less leniency, stricter rules and added prison time. I wondered when their shift changes were, the guards. Shift changes always caused confusion, which would be the best time to run.

Blaze was on my trail. She followed me around the track. I sped up, she sped up. I slowed down, she slowed down. I did the Charleston, she did the ... just kidding.

"Hey, Sallon, right?"

"Mina."

"We go by last names here. I'm Blaze."

"I thought you said we go by last names," I said.

"You look lost the way you be going round the track Sallon, Sallon, quite contrary," Blaze said. "Miss Kelly wants a word, c'mon?"

"I'm not lost. I'm thinking."

"So, that's a 'no'?"

I occupied myself by pretending Blaze was a homeless person that I'd maybe give five bucks to, or buy a sandwich for, and it would be enough zest for her to zip away. Her eyes were glazed, like she had taken too much Zoloft, or too much of something.

Some aunt and uncle in the Deep South brought up Blaze. She shared this information with me when I stuck my neck out for her (and her unborn child). Her father had died when she was a little girl, and her mother was always re-locating for the comfort of the man of the month: Mr. Tennessee or Mr. Kalamazoo. I think the last penis, sorry, place, was Mr. Georgia. She hadn't heard from her mother in a few years, but she spoke of her fondly. Perhaps she was somewhere in the Stockholm syndrome spectrum. Blaze's aunt and uncle had a difficult time raising her, but they were proud of her. They came to visit her when they found the time and put money on her books. That stood for something here.

Blaze scanned the grounds, then handed me a piece of gum like it was methamphetamine. I popped the gum into my mouth without understanding the true exchange.

"Where'd you get that banana?"

"What, are you the fruit police?"

"Miss Kelly likes to be, what do they call it, privy, to exchanges."

It seemed as if the mean pack was toying with the new girl as a form of entertainment.

I said, "I'm not going to be at a bitch's mercy to eat. If you want the banana, feel free. I think it's back in that ditch over there, rotting with everything else in the yard."

Blaze said, "Too much potassium fucks up the heart."

"Well, I guess Miss B wants to fuck up my heart."

At the time I didn't realize that turning down Miss Kelly's invitation meant she'd make me a pawn in her game. It was a serious offense, turning down invitations.

*　　*　　*

In the beginning, letters poured in like wildfire. Most contained good wishes, inspirational thoughts, and cards with happy scenes that people thought would appeal to me in my current state.

> **November 1, 2008:** A pink card with wildflowers said, *I'm not going anywhere. We'll get through this. I promise you. I don't regret being with you or falling in love with you. I think about you every day and think about what I can do to help you get through these tough times.* Love, No name

He was my fiancé, No name, and then he wasn't. I didn't want to grant him a name. I met him through Sami, believe it or not. They worked together. We had planned to get married after I got out, after he finished his doctorate and was qualified to work as a pediatrician. Then we'd have kids: a girl named after my mom, Ella, and a boy named after him, No name. Just joking. But what a crock of shit that was. When he proposed to me, I thought he was joking. When I asked him why he wanted to marry me (after we broke it off), he told me that he didn't want to be far from me. At this time, I felt that he wanted me in a temperate sort of way. I expected that he hung on because he didn't want me to fall. I was right.

> **November 4, 2008:** *I'm sure things are difficult, but I do hope you are managing Mina, my DIVA. It's important to generate public support in situations like these. For instance, creating a Facebook account and asking people*

to join your page, as "fans" will help you. Between exposure like this and my contacts at 60 Minutes, we can generate a sense of public support. I see that public support has something to do with changing the energy of the case. — Isabel Baker

Isabel was a family friend. She was one of those holistic energy healers and an apparent psychic. She was also wealthy and had a lot of high-caliber people in her back pocket. What she didn't know was that I already had a fan.

November 9, 2008: *I saw your story in the paper. I have erotic thoughts of you. It may seem strange, but it's not. Visioning what you cannot see arouses curiosity, don't you agree? I've thought about how it would feel for you riding on top of me, and cumming in you. The longer you're in there, the more it turns me on because I know you'll be nice, and wet, and tight on my dick. Write back – Omar Abbas*

No comment.

November 15, 2008: *Hola Mina, Hope you're feeling better (en salud), let me know if there's good news about your case. Last week I was in jury "F" duty. You know what I mean with the "F" for 7 days. I finished today. Let me tell YOU something. All I was thinking of is your case when I sat on that bench. One feels like a string puppet in a circus. What really pisses me off it's that in the booklet they hand you that reads, "Justice is blind." Behind the judge, it reads, "In God we Trust." Makes one think, what the F. Still praying for you Mina – Isaiah*

Another fan: a sweet one. More of a friend to my mother really, and she wanted us to become "friendlier." In her words, he was a keeper. He was a good person, but I wasn't interested. He was a little desperate for my taste.

November 25, 2008: *Dante, our python, is doing well. He normally stops eating during mating season, from December to May. However, this year he wouldn't eat in May or June… we were growing concerned. We normally feed him dead mice, but this week we tried feeding him live mice and poof! Problem solved. To some it may sound gross, but it's the way things are supposed to be. The only problem is that now he won't go back to frozen mice. We have to stop at the pet store every Tuesday to buy live mice. But the little inconvenience is well worth watching him eat. He really is becoming an awesome hunter! Love Crystal and Cameron*

?????!!!!!!!!!!

November 27, 2008: *Dear Mina, my name is Abida, and I'm a writer and a filmmaker. As you may have already been told, I met with your brother Micah to speak about your case. Your story, which has deeply touched me, was first introduced to me by a mutual friend, Isaiah. He raved about the type of person you are and how you are <u>unfairly</u> facing a difficult time right now. Your brother and Isaiah are interested in having me get your story out. There are several ways I can do that, perhaps a documentary?*

Micah mentioned that you were close to the Middle Eastern community, and I wondered if, although you never visited Iraq, you had any association with that country during that time period and prior. Please share with me whatever is in your heart and mind. I sense having sat with Micah that you come from a good family, which is why I'm also keen to write you and help you. Let's see what can be done, <u>do it</u>, and pray that we have the outcome that gives you and your loved ones peace. Yours truly, Abida.

Abida was a dream, a fellow Iraqi who cared enough about injustice to set my story straight within the Middle Eastern community. She was eager and seemingly trustworthy. Married with kids and a friend to Isaiah. Could I actually capitalize on my charges and punishment? I'll be honest. When I was desperate, vulnerable and not feeling my best, I missed things.

*   *   *

I wasn't feeling my best, so I sought the comfort of God. My mother always said, "God helps those who help themselves." There I was, helping myself. The chapel in the prison, if one could call it that, was profane in nature. It felt like the Temple Mount surrounded by tourist buses, Tommy Bahama shirts and disposable cameras. It also looked as though it was constructed in a matter of days with some makeshift pews, a handful of holy books, and a phony Jesus statue on the verge of keeling over. Someone had spiked him to the wall like they were crucifying him all over again.

Miss B found me idling outside of the chapel and dug her nails into my arm.

"You need to hear the word," she said.

Everyone needed a goddamn word.

We passed a few cons who were praying in pews. One kept crossing her chest, over and over, in true Catholic or Orthodox fashion.

"It's so hot in here. I'm dying," I said.

"Yeah? There are going to be more hot days baby, real hot. Jesus in a tomb for three days hot."

"Is that the word?" I asked.

Miss B pinned me to the wall (under Jesus) and held me there heroically, my uniform clamped tightly in her fist. My heat thumped wildly.

"You wanna' hear the word, huh?"

"What?"

"You a spoiled-ass, prissy-ass little fool."

"What?"

Her grip on me tightened with her tone.

"Keep my name outta' your mouth, bitch. I told your ass day one."

She dropped my uniform, and I thumped to the floor.

"Don't forget what's underneath you."

*   *   *

Miss B was underneath me, in the bus stop, every night. I sometimes craned my neck and checked on her status. More often than not, she was chewing on jellybeans (with her mouth open), and her eyes were like wild currants, red and about to burst.

I wondered if we'd ever be cool again after I "snitched" that she'd given me a banana and Miss Kelly caught wind of it. This solidified that Miss Kelly was a bigwig. That she had the power to alter friendships. Sometime after this incident, I was told that bananas only came in once a month. Bananas were a hot commodity.

"Being on the highest shelf don't mean shit in here," Miss B said.

I couldn't help but feel that she needed a friend. Neither the poor nor the rich had it good in here. So, I told her something that I thought she would have valued.

"The Bible says that the body does not consist of one member, but many. If we were all a single part, like an ear, an eye, a nose, where would that leave the body?" My mother said this frequently and it was one of the only quotes in Corinthians that I could semi-paraphrase.

Miss B didn't respond, but I had hoped that she heard me.

The lights flicked off in sequence.

Chapter 4

More Than a Visitation

Inmates readied themselves for visitation like it was prom. They extracted their cleanest Kentucky State emerald greens, washed and brushed their hair, and painted their faces. There was an air of elation in the bus stop: laughter, lightness and sunshine. Miss B remained rooted to her bunk engrossed in the Bible.

"I didn't know it was prom," I said. Miss B flipped a page silently.

She had heated Downy bottles lodged under her armpits, like makeshift hot water bottles. There were ice cubes under her pits one day and hot water bottles the next. Menopause, much?

Two corrections officers made rounds as watches' alarms sounded: count time. All cons stood for counts in front of their bunks.

"Clear."

*   *   *

Plastic tables and chairs occupied a rectangular room and everything and everyone was visible. The visitation area was a mix between bright eyes, warm smiles and seriousness. The room contained a jumble of emotions and held conversations that could not be expressed over the phone or in a letter.

Cons' eyes veered to the vending machines, which radiated every color of the junk food rainbow: multicolored jelly beans, strawberry fruit gummies, Pringles pizza chips, Blue Bell Gold Rim ice cream, Coca-Cola, Oreo cookies. The list went on. The food machines were the clear focal point of visitation. Some inmates strictly allowed visitors because they wanted processed packages of food that could not be purchased at commissary. The vending machines contained choices that served as an example of freedom, a cornucopia, if you will.

We were told prior to visitation that all inmates had to face the guard station as we interacted with those on our approved visitation lists. The lists contained a visitor's name, address, phone number and the country they lived in. At one time, I had 14 people on my approved list. Did they all come to see me? No, not even close. These friends fell away the longer I was in prison. There was a point in time when people moved on and all that was left was family. Then, only a few family members were left.

An inmate tried to hug who I thought was her boyfriend. "No touching!" a guard screeched.

I jolted, mind racing as I met the eyes of my mom and brother from across the room. My mom cried straight away when she caught sight of me. I must have looked petrified or ghastly. She removed her glasses to wipe her damp eyes. We breathed each other in when I reached her. It was all we could do.

I faced the visitation guard and sat across from my family, as directed. Even in front of me, they seemed so far away. The space between us felt odd. It was such an effort to look at them, like a traffic accident, my eyes peeling back and forth from one to the other.

"I'm sorry, I told myself I wouldn't cry," she clutched her chest.

"It's okay, Mom. I'm okay. Are you okay?" My back was rigid. I thought I'd split from the stiffness.

My mom nodded as my concerned brother rubbed her arm. I could smell her from across the table: vanilla and cinnamon. She smelled of fall. I relaxed a little and surveyed the room. The guard's eyes scanned the space. They were ready to hand out shots like candy on Halloween.

"Where's Dad?"

"Don't take it to heart," my mom replied. She still defended him, even though they had been divorced for a quarter of a century.

They related that he said he couldn't "sit at home" while I was in prison. He was at the Bucca Prison Camp in Iraq at a dusty outpost. Much like my life then, he was stationed behind barbed wire, although he could pass through the checkpoint as he pleased. The post was heavily guarded by the mighty U.S. military, and was packed with American flags, and political prisoners in yellow jumpsuits: blue, red, white, yellow, blue, red, white, yellow.

The story he later told about his work at the camp (particularly how he became the translator for a four-star general specializing in counterintelligence for Iraq) was one he liked to tell and retell, so much so that we had all memorized it. He told us that the general's shoulders were hardened with war but that he was soft-spoken. Dad had met him on a scorching day in the desert.

Little pearls of sweat gathered on his lips. The general turned his back to four translators (including my father) and asked them to translate a poem. The general was interviewing them. They all deciphered the language word for word. The general chose my father. When my father asked why, the general answered, "Your voice. Voices are a powerful thing. They reveal a lot."

Micah said from the table across me, "We're here. Focus on the present." He pulled out a shiny bag of coins and dangled it in front of me. "From millions to quarters," he said, smiling.

"Better to have loved and lost than to have never loved at all," I replied.

We both laughed.

My mother said glumly, "Why are you guys joking around? You're in prison."

"I just want to feel normal again."

"We all do," Micah responded.

"Do I seem different?"

Micah said warily, "You look different; stronger. Do you feel weird?"

"Maybe," I said.

"Maybe," he said.

"Do either of you have cash on you?" The Federal Bureau of Prisons kept tight transaction records. Every deposit and withdrawal had a reference number. Shit, they even kept track of average daily balances. Miss B said that a little something off of the books helped.

"Your greed hasn't waned," Micah said. "Never mind. Forget that I said anything."

I teased my mother to slice the tension. "Avoidance is not the proper way to deal with your emotions."

Micah smiled, "I'll be back." He left to use the facilities. I wasn't sure if Micah needing to use the restroom was a ruse so that my mother and I could have a private moment, or if he had really needed to go.

Either way, my mom came through.

"How much do you need sweetie?"

My mother would have sawed off her foot if I had asked her to. Instead, she became my mule. We did our dirty work in the visitation bathroom to start. It had muted green walls, a cracked mirror, and was always pristine for visitors, which was perfect for getting one's hands dirty. An orderly, the lowest paid position in this facility, cleaned the literal crap out of it. Every clique wanted an orderly in the palm of their hands. It meant they had a route to move products. Visitors would make a drop (money, makeup, sometimes drugs) and orderlies would gather it like squirrels. At this point, I gathered the nuts myself, but in the future, I would hire a squirrel.

My mother wrapped five $20 bills in toilet paper and kissed the package with pink lipstick. I extracted it from a (remarkably full) sanitary napkin box. What was it, a full moon? I shoved it into my bra. It was a rule violation to be in possession of money. Did I care? No.

Micah and I fed the vending machines quarters and ate more food in a couple of hours than I had all week.

Visitors and inmates circled us as the large wall clock's hands looped around. Family and food were a slice of normalcy. Until the visit was over.

My mother said, "We love you so much."

"We're going to get you out, no matter how long it takes," Micah said.

"I thought I'd be out by Christmas."

"You will be. But, if not, don't worry, honey. It will happen," my mother said.

"Is there something I should know?"

"Remember. You're a hammer," Micah boomed.

Chapter 5

Mina "The Other"

The library was the place cons went to cool down. I went there when the repetition of life and the Kentucky heat made me feel sick. Even though it was on the third floor, there was a steep drop in temperature in that room.

Devil's Den was right next door. The place cons went to get hot. The room with the little triangular windows was known to cause fights on the daily. I don't know why the guards kept it unlocked. Inmates attributed ongoing battles to the prison being built on a former insane asylum. Devil's Den was where they had conducted shock therapy, among other patient experiments.

Rumor had it that Devil's Den was alive. People described the room differently, like it had multiple personalities. One inmate depicted it as "cramped and rusty orange in color," while another said that it "talked" to her. Another referred to it as the "yellow room with the breathing walls." Another said that it "had stretch marks dug into the concrete." The room seemed to be ever-changing. My pace quickened whenever I passed it en route to the library.

The library was a different story. It was chill, but still managed to suck the sacred out of escapism with fluorescent lighting, barred windows and locked cupboards. It always managed to whack me back into reality, along with the annoying memoranda tacked to a bulletin board. The latest was, "Keep the windows and doors SHUT! The A/C is on. If you insist on keeping them open, we will turn the A/C off and save the taxpayers of America some money."

I wanted to hook my brain into something, so I scanned the outdated books among emerald-clad inmates. Most chewed the fat and fanned themselves.

Looking around, I imagined that my family and I subscribed to magazines that no one in here read. *The New Yorker*, the *New England Review* and *Forbes* magazine. I decided upon a book called, *After Your Release*. There were slim pickings. I skimmed the material that touched upon halfway houses and supplemental income. One part discussed benefits available to ex-felons. "Federal Legislation states that, because you have been incarcerated (as a result of an emotional problem), you have a DISABILITY and can collect Supplemental Security Income or SSI." So, the government deemed cons as disabled. Ha!

"Please sign this form (stating that you were an emotionally retarded felon) and you'll be granted $360 disability for every month you were incarcerated." Looking back, I remember thinking of what I could possibly buy with that amount every month. I could purchase a plane ticket to Ohio on Spirit. I could also get a manicure and half of a massage at the MGM. I could relocate to Flint and live off of cat food. I must have laughed out loud. Someone mocked me from across the room.

"Ha, ha, ha," Trina said.

The table of African American women stared daggers in my direction, like I had some sort of fatwa on my head. Trina, the Alpha, held her head tipped, like a dog that questioned what its owner wanted. I looked behind me (as most people did in that type of scenario) to find Miss B with her finger in Corinthians.

Back to my book. I ruffled through some pages and read (and re-read) the same sentence over again. "Halfway houses provide skills that formerly incarcerated individuals need to integrate into society." "Halfway houses provide skills that formerly incarcerated individuals need to integrate into society." "Halfway houses provide skills that formerly incarcerated individuals need to integrate into society." Incoming! There it came, the hammering beat of my heart. I didn't know I had such a loud heart until I was pent up in prison.

Blaze was reading up on pregnancy at an adjacent table. I needed a distraction.

"You're pregnant?"

"Mind your business, new fish," Blaze said.

Sharp stares still haunted my periphery.

I said, "Are you getting enough folic acid?"

"Meth is a real drug."

Why were they looking at me anyhow? What could I possibly have that they wanted? Trina smiled.

"Folic acid is for the baby," I said, "to fight against birth defects."

I eyed Blaze's extended belly. She shot over to my table and placed my hand on her stomach. All I could think of was how miraculous it must have felt to have another life growing inside, and how much I had wanted that for myself. I could feel my eyes water.

She said, "What are you, some kind of doctor?"

"Paralegal," I said loud enough for other people to hear.

I had earned my undergrad degree at Mercy College in Detroit. It was a paralegal studies program. Blaze reminded me of a girl I studied with. My ex-friend Dina sat on the stand during our trial as a witness for the prosecution. She said some pretty unsavory things about my character. Anyhow, the paralegal studies program was mostly filled with well-coiffed Black women, so Dina's bleached blonde hair, unpolished nature and crooked teeth stood out in the crowd. She asked me to partner up with her for a project and I didn't protest. I felt sorry for the girl. She worked three jobs to pay for college and lived with her boyfriend (Bob) in some moldy basement filled with $5 wine bottles masquerading as décor. She introduced me to Bob as her "Arab friend."

She said, "Don't worry. She doesn't act like the typical A-rab." I laughed when she said that. I'm not sure why I did; maybe I wanted to be liked by all-American blondes.

At the time, I didn't pay attention to racial profiling. In prison, I had to.

"Why are they staring at me?"

Blaze said, "Two reasons. They want to hurt you, or they want to take something from you. No one knows what you are. You should really hop into Miss Kelly's car."

They called cliques "cars" in prison. There were white cars, mixed cars, and Black cars. If one wasn't in a car, she was considered vulnerable.

Miss B dragged a chair beside me to remove all barriers between us. She picked up my book and gave it a once over.

"Baby, you ain't checking this out. You lost your appeal," she said.

"How the fuck do you know?"

Miss B nodded to the computers. She left the library with her burgundy Bible.

I pulled up the *Michigan Court of Appeals* website and typed in my case number. It stated: Appeal Declined.

My family visited me but kept me in the dark.

*   *   *

At this point, I knew I'd be sucked into the black hole. I'd have to serve my sentence. I wasn't going to get out of it. I lost my appeal. I lost my appeal! There was no amount of money I could have given the government, and there wasn't a lawyer in the world who could have overturned my sentence. They wanted my time.

My heart thumped louder. I lost my appeal. I wanted home. A hot bath, some Pacha, a pack of cigarettes and some Turkish coffee. I wanted to kill Sami. I wanted to kill Sami. I wanted to kill Sami.

If I took my dad's advice, I should have blamed myself for my disappointment and incarceration. But the man screwed me. Yes, I was stupid. I should have gathered more information on him. I should have signed paperwork that stated exactly where the equipment was going. I should have posted the fucking equipment myself at the damned post office. He used me, a fellow country-woman. Maybe that was part of his game to initiate trust. By the way, rerouting the package never impacted him. If I had known then what I know now, I never would have shaken the hand that cemented my captivity.

"Where have your hands been today?" asked the sign above the sinks in the bathroom. I felt the mounting pressure of tears. I didn't want to cry anymore. This was bullshit. All it would take was one person asking how I was doing for me to boil over. A lukewarm shower with low water pressure (among 20 or so glaring eyes) wasn't my idea of a good Tuesday afternoon. It wasn't my idea of a crappy Tuesday afternoon, either. But to the showers I went.

The bathroom held the smell of clothing that had never really dried after being left in the washing machine. It smelled of socks soaked through and of dirty feet. Steam collected in the muggy air. There weren't any vents that I could see, unless they were broken, like everything else in this dump.

I dragged my feet past 30 or so rusty showerheads, residual hair piles and bare con bottoms in a row. Some bums had bruises on them, some had stretched-out tattoos—one lady was inked with the words "till the world blows." Must have been regarding some former lover. "We'll be together till the world blows." Ha, yeah right. Nothing lasted forever.

That day I realized something they had in common. All of the cons had worn, crumpled looks. So many things must have been jostling around in their heads: former pains, discontent; they looked uncomfortable. There was the obvious… no curtains, soap was scarce, hot water was extinct, and $1 shower sandals were a definite must. I wasn't wearing any. I didn't care. But there was something else lurking around in there besides athlete's foot. A vacancy, like something was missing. There was a sad emptiness.

I sat on the toilet seat to do my business that day. It was out of character, I know. I lost my appeal; I couldn't stop thinking about it. I lost my appeal. We had to carry our own rough toilet paper with us. Mine was stolen on numerous occasions. I never thought I'd ever say that, not in a million years. My toilet paper was stolen.

I saw that Miss B was showering, which was a surprise considering how dirty she always looked. We locked eyes for a second, then we drifted back to our own polluted worlds.

I felt gutted like a fish when I stripped off my uniform. I didn't care about nudity or anything else. I lost my appeal. I was stuck here, in this shithole, with these shitty, fucking, low-class, dirty-assed people. I would have to accept the feeling of starting over. Would I? I lost my appeal. I turned on the faucet and watered my face. It wasn't hot or cold. They eliminated choices in here.

I banged my head against the cement. I don't know why I did it. Maybe it was an attempt to get my thoughts out. I did it again and again and again. I wondered if the rust spilling onto my skin was a health hazard. Probably. It tasted like sulfur. I lost my appeal.

I washed away my moods of the past month. The hope that I'd get out before Christmas, gone. The hope that my boyfriend and I would get married next year, gone. The hope that the judge had made a terrible mistake, gone. Blood circled the drain at my feet. Fuck. I had my period. I began to say fuck a lot. I lost my fucking appeal. Fuck!

I stepped out of the shower onto a clump of black hair and wrapped a towel around my head. I noticed that Miss Kelly was stalking me in a mirror. I was always on high alert now. I watched, observed and analyzed (more than usual). A troupe of Black inmates gathered near Miss Kelly, like they were on call. She whispered something to one of them, Trina, who snaked through my fog to deliver the message, like a ghetto Hermes. She covered her mouth slightly as if it lessened the blow of her words:

"You look like them people," Trina said.

"What people?"

"The World Trade Center people."

I yelled, "I am them motherfucking people!"

The Black troupe rose, puffed up their chests, removed their hoop earrings, and inched in on me through the haze. Trina snapped her fingers in my face.

"What does that mean?" I growled.

"Means I'm gunna fuck you up, you terrorist bitch," Trina said.

"Try me."

She clocked me in the face before I could react. I thumped to the floor and held my bloody nose. She stood over me and beat her chest like an animal.

As if conjured up by the devil, everyone circled around Trina and me. They were quiet and calculated … the calm before the storm. It was an initiation into a sickening kind of fight club. They wanted the fight to press on without interference from guards, I imagined.

My adrenaline kicked in as the half-naked cons looked down on me. We threw around more arguments that were more hateful than useful, and I could feel a lot of not giving a fuck coming on strong. I had about enough of everyone's crap, and Miss Kelly really chose the wrong day to fuck with me. I lost my appeal and I had nothing to lose.

"I'm sick of all you niggers!" I screamed.

With this comment, the Black troupe was ready for war. Miss Kelly watched attentively from a safe distance, like the sly Machiavelli that she was. She looked bloodthirsty. Granted, I never should have spewed that word. I wasn't in my right mind that day.

Much to my surprise, Miss B stepped in to save my ass and it wouldn't be the last time. She asked the group, "Why everyone puffed up? Listen, we the real niggers. The real OGs." She pointed at me. "But these guys are the sand niggers. Either way, we all a bunch of niggers, fucked by the system. Man, I need some root beer and ice cream."

Miss Kelly evidently came to her senses and exercised her power in a scolding tone. "That's enough. She's no terrorist."

With that comment, the Black troupe stepped off, hands in the air.

Trina left with the last words, "That's one. Three strikes and boom! World Trade Center ain't got nothin' on me."

Miss B and I left, and she continued to holler. "Detroit finest gone!"

*   *   *

I bought out the commissary on the way back to the bus stop: Pepsi, root beer, Kit Kat bars, Reese's Pieces, Chex Mix, Kettle Pop, strawberry yogurt, and ice cream. I also bought out every variety of cheese: imitation cheese, chili cheese, and mozzarella cheese. Oh, and I scooped up all of the "chicken" selections: imitation white chicken, chicken flavor, honey chicken log, and Chicken of the Sea.

My fairy godmother had put $300 on my books (as a truce) but I still wasn't speaking with her. We'd been sitting across from one another for hours. She said nothing about the appeal. Anyhow, I didn't want to get into a row about it.

Excess anything made me feel better. Just knowing that I had a smorgasbord of junk calmed me down. Usually excess clothing, purses or shoes were on my roster of treats, but in prison, food was it. We kept our bounty in coolers.

Miss B was patiently waiting for me.

"Who was there?"

I felt guilty when I told her. "My mom and brother. Dad's away on business."

Prior to this conversation, she had confessed that she had never had a visitor. Why hadn't her children come to see her? She had 15 brothers and sisters, too. No one had made the trek to Kentucky. Ever.

She paused before she spoke. "You're blessed," she said.

She had already told me some minor things about her family as our relationship knitted itself together. Growing up, her parents were bootleggers with 8th-grade educations. They were hustlers. Her mother also developed an addiction to cocaine, which caused a rift in her marriage. She snorted all of their money. Miss B's father left. At this time, her mother and sister were also in lockup. They were charged with possession of cocaine in Indiana, where she was from. They had been there for some time. Being the eldest, Miss B had to take care of her whole family until she was incarcerated. Now, her 14 brothers and sisters and her two daughters had to fend for themselves.

She rubbed her hands together. "Well, what'd you bring home, baby?" She was wearing a smile, like a kid on her birthday.

I gave her exactly what she had ordered, a 12-pack of root beer and ice cream. She chugged a whole can and burped impressively.

"Detroit's finest! Ain't God good?"

"You stood up for me."

Miss B eyed my commissary, "Girl, you crazy." She extended her pinkie finger. It was juvenile but powerful all the same. "We ride or die, Sallon."

I sealed the promise with my pinkie. "Ride or die. God, I hope we don't die in here."

"We ain't dying in here, baby."

In a bordering bunk, Lucia, a Mexican woman, was moving products. Cons brought her stamps and she exchanged them for food, shampoo and shoes.

"How much does she bring in?" I asked.

"Big money," Miss B said. "Only one in business."

"Conglomerates can be crushed."

"Okay, shot caller, okay. It would take a whole lot of green."

I said, "Green is my favorite color."

"I like red." She held up her Bible.

"I guess we're the Christmas club."

"I'm in for arson," Miss Briana said. Just like that. It was usually the way things went in here. Information just rolled off the tongue when it was ready.

It turned out that Miss Briana got 10 years for an arson insurance scheme. She worked at General Motors as an electrical engineer. Nonetheless, her paycheck wasn't enough to feed 20-plus people.

When Miss Briana was 13, she witnessed her father receive a stack of cash from an insurance company after her childhood home burned down. This proved to be a Eureka moment. Fire equaled money, in her teenage eyes. Aged 20 in 1981, she burned down her friend's house for $30,000. When she had saved $100,000 through her fiery side gig, she bought a farmhouse for her family. One with a wrap-around porch. The success of this inferno led to a chain of flames until 2005. "My brother turned on me. Sent me straight to the feds," Miss Briana said, as if the misfortune wasn't a big deal. "Right before I turned 46. Do you mind if I take my teeth out?"

"No, I don't mind," I said. She popped them out and curled her lip over her upper gums. She stretched out onto her back and held her side. Her face contorted.

"Are you okay?"

"Girl, I'm tired."

"On your feet, inmate," Rachel said, "Grab your stuff."

"Where am I going?"

*   *   *

Miss Kelly's room would be my new nest. It was a 6-person room with three bunk beds. In typical fashion, Miss Kelly read from the *Wall Street Journal*. She always seemed to be concocting some master plan, like an aggressive hunter trying to take down big prey. Blaze sat on the floor in front of Miss Kelly, like the loyal and submissive hunting dog she was. She looked like an Irish Setter. No, she resembled a coonhound: spotted, stubborn and not good off-leash. Blaze looked up at her master. Miss Kelly nodded to the side, and Blaze relocated to her own bed.

I tossed my stuff onto the empty bottom bunk and sat directly in front of Miss Kelly. It wasn't a challenge, per se. It's how I dealt with bullies; how I always had. Dead on. I knew it was only a matter of time before she'd try to sink her fangs in me.

"Welcome home, Saddam," Miss Kelly said.

She busted my balls right out of the gate. When Mr. Clark spoke about this time later on, he said that Miss Kelly said that people called me "a terrorist" and that I should be protected. She claimed that my case was "high profile" and that he'd have "a lawsuit on his hands" if he left me to fend for myself in the bus stop. He respected and listened to her. I wasn't certain why she wanted me in her orb. But I didn't want to stick around to find out.

"Saddam who?" Blaze replied. Miss Kelly waved away her comment like a fly.

I realized in that moment, that Miss Kelly liked Blaze's ignorance. She liked her not knowing who Saddam was. It excited and energized her, like coffee in the morning.

"In here, we have Black cars, mixed cars and white cars. Your people are in the shiny, white Mercedes. I told you once and I'll tell you again. Driving solo doesn't work in prison. Even if you were once capable of conducting 9.5-million-dollar trade deals solo."

She had looked up my case. This was her way of stating that she knew who I was, what I did and how long I'd be staying.

She continued. "If you're in the right car, traffic is mild, and there are more green lights than there are red. And sometimes embargoes take place. Cons step out of their cars. The minute you cross a color boundary, crash! Six years is a long time, Sallon. Miss B isn't your friend. She's a pest at most."

What did spiders do with pests? They ate them. Well, they liquefied them and drank the fluid. I had watched enough of Animal Planet to know a lot about spiders and animals in general (thanks, Mom).

I replied, "Do I look like I have 'sucker' tattooed on my forehead?"

"The 'Other' releases jokes to deflect from seriousness. Interesting."

The Other.

She was attempting to marginalize me. What was an "other," after all? It was someone who was isolated, who didn't quite fit in anywhere. I was the Arab Carmen Miranda without the fruit hat.

She dropped her paper onto my bed before she slunk out of our room, followed by Blaze. She didn't look back. She didn't need to. The front page article blared, "U.S. Air Strike Success Spurs Push for More Iraq Attacks."

*   *   *

I didn't have an appointment, but I charged in anyhow. Mr. Clark was on the phone. He shook his head when he saw me, like I was an annoyance he couldn't shake off. The firm twirl of the phone cord, the thump of setting down his coffee cup, and the crashing of his desk drawers were like a series of small outbursts, as if he dared me to stay in the room. He was always on his high horse, even though he was a minor official that most likely couldn't get onto the police force after his service to America (this ended up being accurate).

"Will do, will do," He said as he hung up the phone. "Sallon?"

My hands flailed and I could feel my face redden. I was used to getting what I wanted. Not anymore.

"You changed my room."

"Yes, I did."

"Without asking? I'm so over this place. The negative energy. There is no civilized way to detox and I'm over the evil woman. Miss Kelly calls me Saddam."

Advice spun off his tongue without much thought; counsel that he had bestowed upon loads of inmates before he awarded me with the privilege of listening to it.

"Stay in the right lane. You're in here for six years."

"Occupy your mind with the outside world, not with what's going on in here."

"Prison is the wrong time to start snitching."

I retorted, "That's your calculated response? What's next, snitches get stitches?"

This sort of interaction was never easy for me. Mr. Clark was a counselor in a women's prison, yet he seemed to be drunk on power. Power over me and power over the other inmates. He could have done whatever he wanted with me.

"Black people are staring at me."

Mr. Clark stared at me. He readjusted his glasses and folded his hands comfortably.

"I heard that people were racial profiling you."

*   *   *

USA VS MINA SALLON — DETROIT, MI — APRIL 2007 — 4:46 PM

She said, "The thing that has bothered me about this case is that the word terrorism seems to overtake everything."

The word terrorism did seem to overtake everything.

I went from zero to terrorist in about five minutes. My eyes must have bulged out of my head when the prosecutor catapulted me into a group with the likes of Genghis Khan and Saddam Hussein. I must have grabbed my lawyer's hand when Ms. MacCann stated this. He must have tapped it professionally before he let it drift back to my side. I clenched my fists. I remember that my hands were cold. Or was it the room that was cold?

When I felt the cold draft, I think I looked back at my mother, who I believe hadn't quite recovered from Ms. MacCann's terrorist accusation. She didn't look quite herself. Her head was tilted when our eyes met, and her ribs inflated erratically. The look she gave me was raw and helpless, like an animal caught in a snare.

Monday snapped, "This narrative is preposterous." He hadn't tried to garner sympathy from the jury yet and MacCann throwing the "T" word around didn't help my case.

She shot back like she had something up her sleeve, "You have an objection specifically to paragraph 9?" She was a regular Rudy Giuliani.

Monday said, "Just that, that there was no trial evidence to support the statement that the equipment was sent to the military, or the Ministry of Communication for the government of Iraq. The end-user was never identified."

"It is my recollection, your honor, that the equipment was sent to the Ministry of Communication for the government of Iraq," *She* said. "That was confirmed in the trial testimony. I don't know that it makes a difference in the sentence today whether it says that or doesn't say that."

Judge Battaglia said, "So, what I'm going to do, because I think it makes no difference in this statement of facts, is simply say the equipment was sent to Iraq. Anything else in the factual statements?"

"No, I just felt duty-bound to point that out," Monday said.

Duty-bound. It was a nice comment on my behalf. But duty-bound didn't save people. Facts saved people. Evidence. Meat.

Judge Battaglia said, "All right. Now let's get down to the meat of the guideline calculations, of which there are some significant objections. We have several base offense levels here. The government proffers 4.1, the evasion of Export Controls, financial transactions with countries supporting international terrorism. There's also mention of 4.2, providing material support or resources to designated foreign terrorist organizations or specifically designated global terrorists, or for a terrorist purpose."

"That clearly is not the offense of which Miss Sallon was convicted," Monday stated.

Monday made an agreement with me before I hired him. He said that he'd get me off on the unjust charges. He promised he would protect me from the prosecutor and the government. He had good reason. Only one other person in the U.S. was sentenced to prison time for violating the U.S. embargo on

Iraq. Most cases like mine were handled administratively, with probation, fines or confiscation. Even Iraq cases that were criminally prosecuted involved no prison time. Monday assured me that I would never set foot in prison.

*   *   *

I sat in Mr. Clark's office thinking about my attorney with the realization that words were just words. Nothing else. Words were just words.

Mr. Clark must have thought it was time to crack a joke when he said, "Our goal is to protect you."

I said, "By bunking me with the anti-Christ?" I started crying. He pushed the Kleenex in front of my hands, on cue.

"If you can prove someone doing something wrong, you can act on it. Miss Kelly is a nice person. She's also very bright. Maybe you'll learn something from her."

"Like how to scare people into submission?"

"Okay, princess. You can file a grievance if you're upset with your room situation, but don't make a career out of complaining. It won't solve anything."

"Not wanting to sleep with the devil doesn't make me a princess."

"That's dramatic."

I said, "What am I supposed to take away from this conversation?"

"Sometimes you have to turn around when you go the wrong way. Don't you call that a 'Michigan U?'"

"The prosecution went the wrong way," I said, "straight up my ass."

"You know how many people in here say that?"

"Verbatim?"

"Verbatim."

I was good at talking with people, great even. I liked it. But I did not like conversing with Mr. Clark. He didn't seem like he wanted to resolve anything. He wanted to get away with doing as little as humanly possible.

Chapter 6

A Field Guide to Surviving Prison

Stay Positive/Act Positive

On the first day of Christmas the government gifted me with six years in a federal prison. It was absolute; cut in stone. There was a chill in the air as I realized the lawyers weren't getting me out. My life before prison suddenly shattered like a glass Christmas ornament at the end of December. But I was trying to stay positive/act positive.

More letters poured in:

> **December 3, 2008:** *This is the straight, unvarnished, albeit welcome truth: you are going to have to make the best of the situation. I am doing what can be done to shorten your sentence. That's really all I can do, and probably all anyone can do. – Loren Monday.*

I felt contaminated when I read this letter. I wanted to rip it to shreds. "Make the best of the situation," my lawyer said. The man to whom I had paid a fortune, someone who said I'd be out by fucking Christmas. I still told myself to stay positive. Monday wasn't my only lifeline.

> **December 6, 2008:** *Who thought getting your situation reviewed would require so much effort? Nonetheless, we push on. – The General.*

My dad asked the General to look into my case. After about a month, the General told my father, "I've never seen a case sealed up so tight before." If a four-star general couldn't nudge Washington, who could? Nonetheless, he continued to seek answers.

December 10, 2008: *Mina, we have another mutual acquaintance! Dina! She called me a few months ago and started the conversation with, "the Indian has 6" (meaning 6 million) and asked what movie I wanted to shoot first. Of course, your documentary came to mind. But I had the gut feeling she was full of shit. She said "Indian 6" sells leather and has stores in Dubai, India and New York. But whenever I asked to meet him, she backed down. I had to stop taking her calls. She seems like a phony.*

I have to say when I read Dina's remarks during the trial, I was disturbed. She was sad to be on the witness stand, as if someone put a gun to her head to be there and say the things she said. And it's very interesting how she can have no memory when it comes to a great deal of incidences but precise memories about what you said with respect to business deals. She isn't an honorable friend, which I hope you find me to be in time. What I want to know is, why the hell you bought her a ticket to London? Your generosity is great, but it seems to be pointed in the wrong direction sometimes. Best, Abida

Dina. I trusted her, once. Before she testified against me. She told the court she was my best friend. Ha!

She had not traveled much and certainly not outside the U.S. I needed some help in London in 2002. It did not go well. She ate too much and with her mouth open at a client meal. She also drank my clients (five Scots) under the table. Who got rip-roaring drunk at a client meeting? Dina did. At one point, she annoyed me so much that I gave her $500 cash and sent her away with a 500-lb. broker to entertain him. I just wanted three hours of peace. She screwed him because she thought he was rich.

At one point after the London trip, I cut ties with her altogether. She was not happy about it. But I just could not take her anymore.

Anyhow, she received a subpoena and told the jury that I spoke about shipping telecommunications equipment to Iraq. Why did she do it? I had ended our friendship due to her tilted morality code.

Earlier, Dina got engaged and fell in love with a Pucci wedding dress. That would have been fine, had her wedding venue matched the dress, like at West Bloomfield's Planterra Conservatory. But her wedding was a scaled-down brunch. Even then, her mom (who she barely spoke to) pulled out of footing the bill and left Dina in the lurch. So, she sobbed and had some other sucker pay for it. This was true Dina fashion. I bowed out of the wedding input when she said she wanted a Renaissance-themed wedding and I had to get my bridesmaid's dress from a catalog called *Witches and Wizards* (I kid you not).

Also, she didn't seem thrilled to be getting married ... nothing like a bride should have been feeling.

So, we trotted out to Lake Orion's Canterbury Village for the wedding. The groomsmen all wore Scottish kilts (even though the groom was Polish), the village was decorated for Christmas year-round, the bridesmaids were gothic, the bride was in a Pucci dress, her mother in a red hat and a silver sequin dress ... for brunch. IT WAS A THREE-RING CIRCUS.

After her husband lost his job, she told me that the only reason she married him was because she thought no one else would. She offered very little support as a wife and continued living like she was single. We went out with some Lebanese guys one night and she hooked up with one, saying, "one day I will land an A-rab."

This one slip turned into full-fledged cheating. She started staying weekends at my condo. One day, I had a heart-to-heart with her. I told her that her marriage was over, that she slept with men she barely knew, drank like a fish, and was never home. She agreed but didn't want to spend money on a lawyer. So, she went to the Oakland County Law Library, filed forms, paid $100 on her credit card, and served her husband with divorce papers. What a gal. But I was to stay positive/act positive. What was something nice about Dina? She had a great smile.

Seems she did land an A-rab after all. I landed right into federal prison.

> **December 14, 2008:** *Mina, my Diva! As I look at your energy, I see that there have been some changes over the past several months. There's lot more yellow and blue in your aura. Maybe you aren't feeling it yet but know that it is there. An inner peace is creeping in – I like it! One thing it will accomplish for you is a change regarding the interaction with others there. There will be an increase in smoother communications. – Isabel Baker*

I told myself that I was to stay positive and act positive. "There will be a change regarding the interaction with others. There will be a change regarding the interaction with others. There will be a change regarding the interaction with others." Maybe if I affirmed this notion it would come true?

> **December 20, 2008:** *First – I LOVE YOU. Second – I <u>do</u> know how you feel, as a mother's heart aches more for her children than anything! We are <u>all</u> working hard 24/7 on the case. I believe there will be a big break soon! Where you are is not pleasant or humane – I get it! I pray for Grandma to watch over*

you, and to keep you well and strong while you are there. Use this experience to make a BIG difference for others. I feel and live your pain. Stay positive/Act Positive. Keep pushing forward. I LOVE YOU. – Mom.

If I stayed positive and acted positive, good things would come, I told myself. "Use this experience to make a BIG difference for others. Use this experience to make a BIG difference for others. Use this experience to make a BIG difference for others."

Bribe Employees

A few weeks into prison, there was an orientation that acclimated unripe cons to their new environment, though some inmates were overripe. I could tell several of them had been locked up before. They were a little too comfortable, with calm demeanors and telltale prison ink. Having a tattoo was like wearing a story. I didn't have any. The elderberry flanking me had a teardrop outline etched beside her eye, "La Eme," across her cheek, and ACAB knifed into her knuckles. Full disclosure: I had Googled prison ink in preparation for prison. The empty teardrop meant that someone was overdue for a murder – yikes! "La Eme" stood for the Mexican Mafia – yikes! The ACAB stood for "all cops are bastards." Okay, that was semi-true (at that time, anyway) before the Black Lives Matter campaign and other activist movements rose to the forefront to combat police brutality.

Apart from the elderberry, about 10 other people were cramped in a dusty room with molded ceiling panels and fluorescents. The hostile lights magnified their battered and broken faces with worry lines, stress acne and scars. Everyone looked unplugged, the last dregs of the day. The elderberry was slouched over a desk. She picked her nose and ate it repeatedly. When people got to a certain age, they just didn't give a fuck.

I knew that if this setting were any indication of my extended stay (reminiscent of a shoddy Super 8) with its meth heads, gang member, hookers, drug mules or dealers lurking about, I'd be in for a real treat. I kept scratching my arms and wondered what kind of diseases I'd carry out of this shithole when I was discharged. *If* I was ever discharged.

Mr. Clark listed a litany of rules and expectations between all the sneezing, sniffling and nose picking. I wanted to punch myself.

Some cons chatted like Mr. Clark didn't exist.

"Pay attention," Mr. Clark raised his quiet voice, which cracked.

A few other department heads joined in the cacophony. The place was incredibly understaffed. Jim the maintenance mechanic was also Jim the electrician and Jim the plumber.

I felt like a child again. Go here; don't go there. Do this; don't do that. Children had rules that kept them safe. "Look both ways before you cross the street," my mom always said. But safety in prison was subjective. The "no touching" rule seemed like a stretch. Sure, cons thought twice before fighting, in fear of getting booted to the hole. But how could anyone get through serving a sentence without being hugged?

Rachel tapped my shoulder when she said, "There is no giving or receiving money, from anyone, at any time. It will put you behind the fence."

Behind the fence meant a maximum-security prison.   Inmates spoke about being "behind the fence" like it was cancer. Miss B once said, "Don't be mixing with bad people. The camp be heaven compared with what's behind the fence." And she knew. She had been behind the fence, over the fence, around the fence and under the fence.

Mr. Clark said, "Familiar faces haunt me. I want to send out a better product into the world. That way, you don't come back. I don't want you back. I got a line out the door."

He was right. The recidivism rate in the U.S. was ridiculous. Most inmates ended up back in prison. The system was set up for failure. Mr. Clark told me later that, "in most countries, prison is the place you send failures. In America, society itself is failing." He also told me that a quarter of the world's prisoners were imprisoned in the U.S. I wasn't sure how true that was, but it seemed accurate.

I chimed into the chaos. "How much do I have to pay to get out of that door?" I scanned the room for an affirmation, a "hell yeah," or an "amen." Instead, my outburst was met with cold eyes and crickets. Elderberry smiled at me. It wasn't a friendly smile. It was a smile that had nothing to lose.

Rachel closed the session with highlighting other sinful violations that would send you behind the fence: *possession of stolen property, disobeying direct orders, creating a disturbance, destroying property* and *bribery of an employee…* to name a few.

*   *   *

The only decent thing about having to deal with Mr. Clark was the air conditioning. We were back in his office for another hour-long session. It was required. Mr. Clark's eyes looked dilated and he was distracted. He was also suffering from another big *d* word.

Divorce. Miss B told me that he was going through a divorce and that he was hooked on oxy. She also said, "That lil niggie won't last much longer in here." I asked her how she knew. She replied that small things revealed a lot. One small thing was that he had removed his wedding band. I stared at his bare ring finger and waited for the unsolicited advice.

"The difference between you and I is one decision."

"I told you once and I'll tell you again," I said. "I don't deserve to be here."

"You how to get out of that door? You do your time."

"Can I just slide you some cash or a gift card to punt me out of this place?"

"Make it a $200 dollar gift card to buy my kids some shoes and you got yourself a deal."

"You have kids?"

"Two. The only things I own outright in this world."

"I wanted kids," I said.

"Someday you will," he said.

"I'm 36."

"There are many options these days. We did IVF."

"So, all it takes to jet out of here is a gift for your kids?"

He sent me a polluted look. "What do you want from me?"

"Conversation," I said. "Conversation and air conditioning."

He said, "I just fixed it."

"Good, you need to cool off."

He laughed. He actually laughed. I broke him.

"When you get out, I'll take you up on that gift card," he said.

Mr. Clark later told me that, after this meeting, he read my file, including some articles about my case. He realized that things didn't add up.

*   *   *

USA VS MINA SALLON — DETROIT, MI — APRIL 2007 — 4:50 PM

She said, "The first element is that the defendant conspired to violate the trade embargo on Iraq. What's a conspiracy? A conspiracy is an agreement. Now, it doesn't have to be a written contract. In fact, it doesn't even have to be spoken. It's a meeting of the minds to violate the trade embargo on Iraq. Not all the details of the conspiracy need to be planned out or laid out ahead of time, but the crux of it, the violation of the embargo has to be in place. And the other thing you'll hear the Judge tell you about conspiracies is that if you find that two people joined a conspiracy, those individual conspirators are responsible for the reasonably foreseeable acts of each of the other conspirators, even if that person didn't necessarily participate in that act or didn't know what was going on."

Monday said, "There were no offices or cubicles at Curve Tech; business was conducted right out in the open. Why is that important? Well, let's apply our common sense. If you're involved in criminal activity, you're just going to do it out in the open? Leave papers around for everybody to see? Talk to your coconspirators on the phone where other employees are going to be able to overhear? Does that make sense?"

Basically, this charge of conspiracy meant that everyone this deal touched was on the boat, and I was driving when it went down into the deep. And, as my brother said, "You can sink, or you can try to save."

*   *   *

After I was sentenced and my case was sealed, Sami Al-Mufti's guilt decided to write a declaration of his own accord. He thought that it would save me. Shortly after, he asked if I would consider doing business with him in the future. Was he serious? Was his letter a bribe for me?

> *Declaration of Sami Al-Mufti:*
> *I, Sami Al-Mufti, solemnly declare, under penalty of perjury under the laws of the United States of America, as follows:*

> 1   *Sometime in 2002, approximately one year after I signed a contract with the Iraqi Ministry of Communications to supply a GSM system in Iraq, a contact was established by American agents, who said to me that they worked for the CIA.*
> 2   *I continued to meet with these agents two at a time, approximately four in number, on a regular basis until approximately two or three months before the invasion of Iraq in March 2003. We met in hotel rooms and cars in Amman, Jordan, where I was then living.*
> 3   *These agents told me that they wanted my cooperation so that they could use the system for their own purposes. It was agreed between these agents*

and me to utilize the GSM system to track Saddam Hussein and his military aides and to listen to certain conversations.

4   *The agents did not tell me specifically that their intended use of the GSM system was classified or an unclassified operation, but they did emphasize that they wanted their involvement kept secret for their own safety and mine. In fact, they asked if I had told my wife about our meetings, and when I said no, they were pleased.*

5   *In 2002 during a meeting with a CIA agent who identified himself to me as "Jim," and with whom I had met with several times, I was assured that and told, "We are not after you, we are not after anyone you are working with, nobody will get hurt, nothing will happen, we just want Saddam and his henchmen."*

6   *I was never offered payment for my cooperation and did not ask for any. However, in September or October 2002, the agents provided me with the names of Lebanese engineers who were to help work on the system, and asked me to get Iraqi Visas for them, which we did. The engineers visited me in my office in Amman and I gave them the Visas.*

7   *The American agents also promised to provide specific (special) software for the system, but this never happened, because the invasion came first.*

8   *Approximately four and a half (4.5) years ago, to the best of my memory, Special Agent Ward attempted to contact me. Special Agent Ward contacted my niece, and she gave me the contact details and message of Agent Ward. I spoke to Agent Ward and, in this conversation, he began asking me about the Mobile GSM and I was hesitant to talk with him and asked him who he was and what agency he was from.*

When Special Agent Ward indicated he had Security Clearance and had seen the file and indicated he knew about the GSM, it was based on this disclosure that I felt more comfortable having discussions with him.

The next conversation was in 2004, from my recollection, the day after Special Agent Ward had searched the office of Curve Tech. Special Agent Ward was asking questions about Mina Sallon, if she knew the equipment was for Iraq and I said no, to the best of my knowledge, she did not, and I never told her.

Another conversation with Special Agent Ward was approximately 2008 and he asked me if I could come over to the United States. Special

Agent Ward also asked me if I would authenticate a statement or a document and also asked if we could meet at the Embassy in Madrid to sign some papers. Special Agent Ward also sent me emails in 2008.

9   *When I spoke to Mina Sallon's lawyer before the trial, I did not tell him about any CIA involvement because I believed the information was secret and was concerned for my safety if I admitted it publicly. I told her lawyer that I feel guilty for all of the legal troubles brought on to her. Even now, I am concerned that by admitting that I was working with the CIA, I am putting myself, my family, and many other lives in serious jeopardy. In fact, I believe that it would not be safe for me to go to Iraq or the Middle East, and I would have problems with some people in Jordan as well. I also believed that justice would prevail in the United States of America in this case, but it did not, despite my efforts to explain to Judge Battaglia in the best way I could at the time.*

I declare, certify, verify, and state under penalty of perjury under the laws of the United States of America that the foregoing is true and correct to the best of my knowledge and recollection.
Signed, Sami Al-Mufti

The letter came too late. For him, the timing was perfect, as it would never be on record in the court system. Did I think the timing was an accident? Hell, no.

The timing was perfect.

*   *   *

Possess Money

People added up everything in prison: cash, infractions, cash, favors, cash, commissary, cash and time. One day I realized that a year had gone by. I had ticked off 365 days on my bunk. It was a Tuesday, and the bus stop was overpopulated in between counts, which meant people were wheeling and dealing.

Miss B and I stared at Lucia as she made money moves. The elderberry (Lucia's right-hand) was on high alert. Her ears perked up like a Border Collie guarding its prized pig. Lucia passed the elderberry stamps, which were payment from her customers. The elderberry passed her a sandwich. She gorged on the sandwich and had a burger on deck.

I couldn't imagine Lucia's ass getting any bigger than it already was. She had commissary out the ass. There were certain foods that inmates could only reach through the visitation vending machines. Sandwiches and burgers (only available on Tuesdays) were the popular choices. All types of proteins went quickly in prison, mostly because they were the white whales of the food choices. They could also be used for flavoring other meals, like packaged soups, potato logs, pizzas, and whatnot.

Miss B said, "That's livin' in prison. Eatin' meat. Shows you got it going on."

"I would want to be paid in cash."

"Commissary is where it's at, Detroit. You can't eat cash."

I opened my cooler, which didn't have a lot going on. It was the end of the month and my commissary account was not only meatless, but it was also dry. The trouble was that we were only allowed $300 on our books, which my mother placed in my account every month. I stared at a lonely Pepsi and a sole granola bar. I handed over the Pepsi to Miss B, which she happily accepted. She passed on the granola.

"Don't eat rabbit food," she said.

"I've never heard of a rabbit eating granola."

"You never had been to the 'hood, baby. Rabbits eat whatchu give 'em. Rabbits, kids, grown folk. They hop into dumps, garbage bins, steal from BBQs, you name it."

Animals ate what you gave them. Ding, ding, ding. Cons weren't any different. I thought back to middle school, when I got my hands on hard-to-obtain goods, the rare items kids went nuts over. My heart skipped a beat.

"How would I get something like earrings or Pureology shampoo?"

"You talkin' bout outside items. Black-market items?"

"I guess."

Miss B explained, "We got white market: That's commissary. Grey market: That's stuff from visitation vending machines. It's worth double, baby. Black market: I know you ain't talking about drugs, but earrings is the same charge… that'll get you in trouble."

"I'm already in trouble."

"I'll get you whatchu need, Detroit."

Right then and there I decided to start a business. Some things never changed.

I said, "How much money do you make, Miss B?"

"Fifty dollars a month," she said proudly.

"I piss on fifty dollars. I'll give you double."

"What are we going to do?"

"Put Lucia out of business."

She held her Pepsi up to meet my granola bar. Cheers!

"We should eat a sandwich or something," she said.

"Whoever found happiness in a sandwich?"

My mother always said, "Use your experiences to make a big difference for others." But what kind of difference could I make with $300 on my books? Possessing actual cash meant more time. You heard it from Rachel. As Mr. Clark once remarked, however, "If you can prove someone doing something wrong, you can *act on it*." If you can't prove anything, you don't have a case."

*   *   *

Miss B said, "If you ever want to say somethin,' do it during face-to-face time. Feel me?" I felt her. Phone calls were logged, and letters were copied. It didn't take a genius to figure that out. Real conversations took place at visitation, with family.

One day at a visitation I told my mother that cash was queen, and cons could do more with it. She told me not to call myself a con. She was in denial. I also related that money on the books wasn't as valuable, although I needed that, too.

I didn't want any red flags on my revamped, entrepreneurial ass. The $300 on my account every month was a pattern that Miss B said, "needed to continue."

"You're asking mom to break the law? In prison? That's rich," Micah said.

I bit back, "Don't worry, you'll be acquitted."

My mom cut in, "Okay, okay. Mina, honey, are you washing your hair?"

"No, the shampoo here sucks."

"You're entitled," my brother said. "You don't deserve more than anyone."

"I don't deserve to be in here!"

The guard's head snapped toward our table; I eased him with a grin.

"Okay, kids, that's enough," Mom whispered. She always wanted to put on a public showing of sanity.

Micah leaned forward. "You know what I think? I think *She* was easy on you."

"I think *She* was easy on you," I shot back, "You're selfish."

"You know what I want? I want a friend that doesn't ask me about you. I'm so sick of it. Talking about you. Looking at you. Writing senators. You think you're the only one in prison? Think again, Mina."

Confrontation wasn't his strong suit. My brother was still tethered to me and the case. He had tried to distract himself while I was imprisoned in any way he could. He got a pilot's license, an actual, fucking pilot's license. He flew a Cessna RG something or other. My mom sent me a photo of it. He also wrote more than 12 books. The genius stayed busy. I knew he felt responsible for my sentencing, but what did he think he was going to do with a plane? Land on the campground and soar me out of there like El Chapo?

Losing also wasn't Micah's strong suit. He couldn't accept that we lost the trial. That he had missed some sort of equation in his business model that drove it into the ground. And that he lost the appeal of my sentence. He wrote a ton of Senators and Congressional reps. and media people. He made calls. To basically anyone who would listen. So did my mother and father and friends. How many did we hear back from? Zero.

The letters went a little something like this:

> *Sensitive Information of an Urgent Nature.*
>
> *To whom it may concern, I request your immediate assistance in an urgent matter concerning a great miscarriage of justice. My sister/daughter/friend was imprisoned with alleged export violations. However, the jury and defense wasn't privy to certain information. The individual (Sami Al-Mufti) who contacted my sister/daughter/friend to arrange for the exportation of telecommunications equipment was a CIA asset. The CIA asset told my sister/daughter/friend that the equipment was going to Turkey, not Iraq. Also, the CIA asset, a renown international businessman, is so troubled by my sister/daughter/friend's wrongful conviction that he executed a sworn statement and is willing to testify in any legal proceeding concerning my sister/daughter/friend's innocence, even though this testimony would adversely impact his ability to conduct business in the future and potentially endanger lives. The government and the judge (in this case) were aware of the CIA's involvement. However, the records were ordered "sealed" and this information was not disclosed to the jury.*
>
> *I would ask your assistance in reviewing this case — Micah, Ella, Mansur, or friend.*

I told Micah, "You're free to leave." It was a low blow. It's what the judge said to him when he was acquitted.

With that, Micah got up and left. Engineering genius that he was, he couldn't solve the algorithm. It drove him mad. The problem was still behind bars and he didn't want to look at it anymore.

My mom gave me the cash. I paid Miss B her monthly fee. We shook hands.

*   *   *

Prison was a business and we had to make all of our clients happy. And for whatever reason, Miss B and I were a good team. I knew how to make money, or, in Miss B's words, I knew "how to make a business out of everything." And Miss B had been around the block. She knew how to move stuff around and how to play people. She was what people in prison called a fence. Everyone went to her when they needed something. And she knew exactly what everyone needed. We were a good combination plate.

"We buy out the food source," Miss B said over breakfast. "Make all those little piggies come runnin.'"

Miss B popped the microwave door open in the mess hall. She tossed in a couple of raw eggs and set the timer for five minutes. We watched the ovals spin around. Watching food was a common practice.

"Buy out commissary? You nuts? They'll kill us."

We stared at two male painters rolling paint over the wall in a new shade of bland. Most cons watched them and catalogued their images (for their spank banks). There wasn't a lot going on in terms of male imagery or male attention.

The guards decided that for whatever reason the mural in the mess hall (the jungle of trees and animals) should be painted over. That art, or any sort of thing that created life, could and would be obliterated. The inmates had designed the mural before I had arrived. Miss B said that it "boosted morale." She must have heard that from a guard. Truly, it was another thing that the guards could take away from the cons as a form of punishment. Misbehavior equaled the subtraction of privileges and/or anything that sparked joie de vivre.

Boom! The eggs exploded along with our pride. A couple of cons hit the floor. Shit! I apologized to the cons in the vicinity.

Trina rose from the floor, "Fuck you, man."

"Don't worry," Miss B told me. "Soon she be so far up our asses, like a hooker."

"Sexy. How?"

"New protein coming in today: bacon! We're going to nab it!"

"How do you know that?"

Miss B tapped on her bible.

I said, "Glad the big guy is talking to someone."

Miss B looked at Trina and her pack of dogs and said, "Ima take your source. Make you come to me, bitch."

*   *   *

We checked off our wish list on the commissary sheet: 50 packages of microwave bacon. I handed the sheet to the inmate manning the commissary box when we made it to the front of the line. She gave it a once-over.

"That's a lot of ham for one human," she said.

"Only God can judge me."

The commissary inmate pushed 40 out of the 50 packages to me. Christmas came early and I wasn't on the naughty list this time.

Miss B high-fived me. "Yes!"

*   *   *

The next day we made our way back to the mess hall, and back to the microwave with our prized protein. The mural was now fully covered, and a lot of cons were pissed about it. There was a hushed and hostile energy in the room. The calm before Big Wheel Parrish stepped up to his position behind the plate at the home opener. Tigers' fans idolized him, and competing fans wanted to annihilate him.

Ding, the microwave sounded.

Miss B yelled, "Free bacon, comin' in hot!" She was like an announcer at the baseball game. "I see Ruth from Philly stepping up to the plate. Next to bat, we have Blaze!"

Cons stormed the microwave like they would a hot dog stand at the World Series, including Trina.

Miss B danced around. "Pull up on me," she yelled. I had never seen someone so excited before. She saw something that I didn't. She always saw through people. The bases were loaded.

"Don't butt in fronta' me, bitch," Trina barked at another con. She held her palm out like I owed her something. I hesitated. Miss B nudged me. I fed the enemy. She pounded my fist: respect.

Miss Kelly stood back and watched the action at first base. The quiet protein quarrels with the umpires (Miss B and I), the crisp bites of bacon in happy mouths, the cons standing in line for seconds, the bacon slipping out of hands – fly ball! And the newborn respect. I could hear my father's voice in this moment. "For free, Mina? Never feed people for free; they'll never leave you alone."

Miss B concluded our victory with, "The first time is always free! Need somethin,' you know who to call!"

The bacon was our business card. Miss B said that it sent the message that we could get our hands on what cons wanted, "flavor." And just like that, my stock value rose. "Businesses have to spend money to make money," my father always said.

*   *   *

USA VS MINA SALLON — DETROIT, MI — APRIL 2007 — 4:56 PM

She said, "Where is the money? $9.5 million just doesn't disappear. Where is the money?" *She* actually made her way up onto her desk in the courtroom. (Power suit on full display. I think the suit was green. No, it must have been gray.) *She* shouted it at the jury. Yes, she stood on her desk, in her brown, scuffed flats. What a spectacle.

*   *   *

The money was gone, bitch. *She* could see that clearly via my bank statements. The prosecutor and the government had always had my complete cooperation.

Loren Monday said, "Want the coat off her back?"

The first deal with Sami Al-Mufti was worth $4.9 million. I called the U.S. Department of Commerce to ensure that the export (from the UK to Turkey) was legal: It was. I had also asked Sami to sign an affidavit that solidified where the equipment was going (he was happy to sign it). So, I handed off the shipments to Sami and I'll admit that I wasn't entirely aware of what the labels said. I trusted Sami. Sometimes I didn't even see the equipment. Sami could have easily stamped on a hidden destination. How was that my problem? Sounded like a Sami problem.

The second deal was worth around $4.6 million, which is how the prosecutor reached $9.5 million that *She* shouted from the rooftops. However, by the time Curve Tech paid off everyone involved in the deal, what was left in my personal account was $300,000, which was later almost completely depleted by legal fees. Yes, I went from having $300,000 in my account to about $3,000, and then ended up with $300 in prison.

She said, "We saw bank accounts, not only in the United States but in the United Kingdom, in the United Arab Emirates, in Spain, and in Jordan. We saw evidence that the amounts in the accounts were structured into small amounts for the paper trail. On one particular day, $1.5 million was transferred to Sami Al-Mufti, but they broke it up into three separate transfers of $500,000 each and sent the increments to banks in different countries, in the UK and the U.A.E., because it would look better."

Loren Monday said, "There were indeed offshore bank accounts, which is really no more than you would expect to have when you're dealing with people who are based, or companies that are based, offshore. This is not a situation where a person takes money from the United States and moves it offshore in order to secret it. Here, the money had to go out of the country because that's where the goods were located, that's where the customer was. That was the nature of the transaction. It had nothing to do with money laundering. This was an entirely straightforward series of transactions. Funds for purchases were transferred via the conventional means of wire transfers, not through nominees, not through third parties, not in layered series of obfuscations, but from the buyer to the broker and then either to the seller or the transporter and back to the broker, and I'm sorry, back to the customer if funds weren't used. There was nothing like the kind of layering or deceit or deception that the sophisticated international money launderer would be expected to use and to be punished more severely for it."

*   *   *

Before the trial, *She* told the bank to freeze my account. My teller, a middle-aged white man, had told me he received a notice from the prosecutor as we sat in his office, which was a neutral room with framed photos of his beaming wife and kids, all in some hue of khaki. He passed me a Post-it note:

"I'm not going to do it."

He slipped me what was left in my account, about $3,000.00 (minus a dollar) with a sly look on his face, like he'd be talking about this lapse in protocol for the next decade. I bit my no-name cookie and washed it down with Folgers coffee. I signed my name. Sorry, but I wasn't going to give up what was left of my hard-earned cash.

"We hear you're going to prison," he said before he "froze" the pennies left in my account. I hadn't made a house payment in four months and he knew something was off. Everything was off.

*　　　*　　　*

It didn't take long to decipher that prison was an enterprise and its product was people: inmates. The minute I stepped into my workplace back in 2008, the kitchen, with its lead-painted walls and expired food, I realized I was in a fucking prison camp.

Most inmates owed restitution and they were paying it back with their measly $20-50 a month. (Miss B had to pay $25 per month, as did I.) God, cons would never, ever, ever be able to chop enough carrots, scrub enough floors, or wash enough prison uniforms to pay the debt. The government owned them. The government owned me. The government had inmates exactly where it wanted them, stuck in the system and indebted to them.

Miss B and I both worked in Food Services. She washed dishes and I did food prep, mixing ingredients, and the never-ending cycle of chopping of onions. Onions were a staple in prison, enough to make everybody cry. They were cheap. Just like everything else.

On a Saturday, I opened an expired box of pancake mix to discover a cockroach. A fucking cockroach! I was extremely bloated. I hadn't taken a shit in three fucking days. Being backed up didn't help my migraines, either. A cockroach in the mix would have been too much for anyone.

"We can't eat this! Is everyone seeing this?" I screeched. I felt like I was going to puke. I wanted to die.

All of the Food Service workers carried on. They'd seen it before.

I didn't stop. "It's a fucking cockroach in the pancake mix!"

Miss B said, "Baby, you know how many roaches I ate in my day?" She took off her rubber gloves and laid them on the food prep station. They drip, drip, dripped all over the floor.

"Going to mop that up?" I asked.

"Nope," she said. "But I will take that sandwich you've been carrying around in your pocket." This girl always had to have something in her mouth, I swear to God.

"How in the hell do you know that?" She had sharp eyes. You couldn't get anything past Miss B. I handed her the sandwich. It was the Friend-for-Food program.

Back in 2006, I was involved in the Oil-for-Food Program for Iraq. It was a program set up by Bill Clinton. Basically, Iraq sold oil in exchange for goods to meet the needs of Iraqi citizens. It was designed to alleviate suffering (after America pillaged their country for weapons of mass destruction). Nonetheless, I can tell you that the food America sent to the assumed enemy (Iraq) was 10 times better than the food that it fed its own incarcerated citizens.

I looked over all of the pancake boxes, all expired, all probably roach-infested, and all without a lick of fiber. I moseyed over to the bin and threw them in. Fuck that.

Out of the corner of my eye I saw Blaze, in the hallway, with Rachel and a skinny white couple. As they made their way to the kitchen, I noticed the Bibles in hand and wooden crosses dangling from their necks. They were probably surviving off of communion, the body and blood of Christ.

They shook hands with Blaze and left before she ransacked the kitchen, famished. She opted for her usual morning breakfast special, scrambled eggs. Miss Kelly and her girls had a plethora of privileges.

"Your aunt and uncle visiting?"

Blaze said, "That's what they told me to say." Her eyes were the usual shade of fucked up.

I said, "Rachel?" with light-years of disdain. Blaze nodded.

Miss B said, "I know where this is going."

Blaze had her baby back in August. Because she hadn't researched or organized anything prior to the baby being born, the baby ended up at the office of children's services. I heard that some prisons allowed cons to keep their babies behind bars. This prison wasn't one of them.

"They want to adopt the baby," Blaze said. "The chaplain and his wife."

"Turn it into a little Bible-belt holy roller," Miss B said in between bites of my pre-packaged, high-preservative and highly salted sandwich.

Blaze diverted her bloodshot eyes from Miss B to her Bible, delicately placed above the sink. It was always left within eyesight and always a little bit out of reach.

"What's wrong with people that live by faith?" she said. "Faith moves mountains." Blaze was always copying what people said, what Miss Kelly said, or what books said, the Bible, in this case, like she didn't have a mind of her own.

Miss B coughed, she held up a finger and coughed some more. Coughing hurt her back and she regularly placed a hand on it like a Band-Aid. "There's a reason they be in church so much. Know what I mean? Church full of sinners: big ones and small ones, but mostly big ones. Chaplains ain't any different."

"He said he was going to get me a job when I get home," Blaze said. "That a job is no problem for God."

I said, "What the fuck does that mean?" Miss B and I had a good laugh.

More of the chaplain's words spewed from Blaze's mouth. "That God will meet your needs. He works according to your faith level."

"For God, a job is no problem," I said. I couldn't stop laughing. "A job, a mansion and a Mercedes. No problem! Just get your faith up!"

"God helps you if you help yourself," Blaze said.

Miss B said, "Did he say what kind of job he going to get you?"

"No."

Miss B said, "Sounds like he be skirting around the job part. Sounds like it's a bribe to get that baby in his hands, or in his church or somewhere else. Perverts be popping up like groundhogs, especially Catholics. Is he Catholic?"

I said, "what about your actual aunt and uncle?" My stomach growled.

"You okay, Sallon?"

"I'm a long shot from okay."

"I don't wanna put it on them. I'm enough to deal with," Blaze said. "I can't get ahold of my mom."

"The same mom that abandoned you?" I said.

"She has commitment issues," Blaze said.

"Un huh," Miss B said.

"I'm a drug addict and I can't afford to support my kid. She needs a good home."

"It sounds like they're really pushing you to give her up," I said.

"Making you into a bad mama before you even tried," Miss B said between pauses of hacking up her lungs.

"You know," I said, "You can give your aunt and uncle power of attorney until you get out." I was open to feeding the enemy. "Never put all of your eggs in one basket," my father said.

Blaze said, "What's that?"

I tried telling the substance abuser what was what. "It means you place the baby into their custody, their care, temporarily, for a short time… until you're released. Just think about it."

Blaze handed me her plate. "I'd be stressed, and I wouldn't want them raising her *their* way. It would be a lot of 'Get me this, and do that, and come home before 12.' Soon, she'll be turning tricks to get outta' the house and I don't want that life for her."

Miss B and I looked at each other. Was she out of her mind?

"Can I borrow five bucks?" She looked at me with sad eyes.

"You want money?"

"I'll pay you back when my aunt fills my books."

Miss B pulled me off to the side, "Don't dip into the business."

"She has a kid." God, I hoped that she didn't spend it on drugs when I gave it to her. Five bucks went a long way in prison. But who could be sure? Truthfully, I felt powerful when I was able to give a little something to someone. I had missed that feeling.

"Thanks, Sallon," Blaze said. "You're a good egg."

Camilla, the kitchen boss, charged into our conversation. "Where the fuck are my pancakes?"

Both Miss B and I shrugged.

"You're on the out," Camilla said, "the both of you." Camilla pushed my shoulder, the bad one. The push wasn't hard or soft. It was just enough of a push that I slipped on the floor, on Miss B's fucking water puddle, and my 180-lb. ass fell right onto my fucking wrist.

"Fuck!" I screamed. I did a lot of tumbling in prison.

Miss B came to my aid. "It's not broken," she said before helping me up. She gave my wrist a once over, "Good as new."

"Hardly."

"You ain't dead," Miss B said.

"Clean up your fucking mess next time."

Miss B saluted me, "Aye, aye captain."

"Oh," Blaze said, "Miss Kelly wants carrots. A lot of them."

Miss B and I both rolled our eyes. I stretched my hand.

"She gunna pay this time?"

Blaze said, "She won't organize a rape," before she bounded out the door.

Our occupations were handy for business and our personal lives. We could exchange stuff like carrots for not being raped. But, inhaling lead paint all day (yes, I read the ingredients on the paint can) wasn't top notch for one's lungs, either.

What's more, the asbestos didn't help. The building we were living in was ancient. Miss B said that a few years back, the warden tested for it. A guard had developed asthmatic symptoms. But they did nothing with the positive results. In fact, a Congressman O'Brien took a tour back in July and they wouldn't let him onto the 3rd or 4th floor. There was asbestos all over the place. Asbestos was, after all, a cheap way to fireproof the joint. It also wasn't illegal in the U.S. until the mid-70s, although it caused a multitude of health issues, mostly aggressive forms of cancer. It took a toll on cons' lungs. Miss B coughed like there was no tomorrow.

Nonetheless, kitchen work also gave me an inside scoop with regard to what the U.S. fed inmates: pre-packaged, sodium-packed, obesity-charged, cheap crap. Did I mention that I hadn't had my period in eight months and that I was now 180 lbs.? After being exposed to enough garbage and my fair share of stomach pains, I tried to change the menu.

I wrote up what was called an "Inmate Request to Staff," as recommended by Mr. Clark. It was addressed to the man in charge of recreation, Mr. Thomas, who had just conducted a speech with respect to wellness and recreation. The presentation was banal; probably recycled from 1990 and something that was organized via an old-school PowerPoint presentation. He read right off the slides. "We offer life-changing wellness services…" Right.

> *Dear Recreation/Wellness – Mr. Thomas, I was wondering if it is at all possible that we integrate more healthy products or protein-based nutritional items as part of a complete wellness plan. Such items as protein shakes and dietary supplements could either be added as a SPO (supplier purchase order) or as a premium pay item at commissary. Ultimately, the addition of these items (and ones like it) would promote wellness. It is difficult to try to maintain wellness in prison when items such as powdered sugar and beef/chicken bouillon (which are heavily immersed in MSG, saturated fats and sodium) are a staple in our diet. Scientifically speaking, protein aids in fat reduction (particularly belly fat), which is linked to an array of diseases, such as diabetes and heart disease, which is why it should be on the menu. All in all, we don't have enough protein-packed items to produce a proper wellness plan – Mina Sallon*

Mr. Thomas' response: *Talk to Medical!*

> *Dear Medical – Mr. Bugard, I was wondering if it is at all possible that we integrate more healthy products or protein-based nutritional items as part of a complete wellness plan. Such items as protein shakes and dietary supplements could either be added as a SPO (supplier purchase order) or as a premium pay item at commissary. Ultimately, the addition of these items (and ones like it) would promote wellness. It is difficult to try to maintain wellness in prison when items such as powdered sugar and beef/chicken bouillon (which are heavily immersed in MSG, saturated fats*

and sodium) are a staple in our diet. Scientifically speaking, protein aids in fat reduction (particularly belly fat), which is linked to an array of diseases, such as diabetes and heart disease, which is why it should be on the menu. All in all, we don't have enough protein-packed items to produce a proper wellness plan – Mina Sallon

Mr. Bugard's response: *Talk to Wellness!*

It was Corporate America in a nutshell. It was a circular system where the hardworking peasants (cons) got knocked down and the kings and queens (the warden, guards and counselors) sat back with their semi-cushy salaries and did sweet dick all day long. God forbid the kings and queens step off of their thrones and reach beyond their job descriptions.

Bureau of Prisons Health Services, 2009	Inmate Name: Sallon, Mina Description	Reg # 30810-039 Type
Health Problem 11/1/09	ADHD *we do not medicate	Chronic
Health Problem 11/1/09	Common migraine	Chronic
Health Problem 11/1/09	Chronic Pain Syndrome	Chronic
Health Problem 11/1/09	Shoulder Pain	Acute
Health Problem 11/1/09	Dyspepsia (stomach pain)	Chronic
Health Problem 11/1/09	Injury to hand (bruising only)	Reesolved
Health Problem 11/1/09	Bronchitis	Acutee

*   *   *

One afternoon, Miss B and I fell into the kitchen freezer and decided to sample the product. Another afternoon, we sampled it again. Okay, it became a habit. Miss B knew how to unlock doors and this one wasn't any different. I was tired of being "the product." I busted my ass and what was it for? We were already on the out (kitchen jobwise) and I wasn't going to convince Medical and/or Wellness and Recreation that we needed more than MSG to survive.

"The ice cream is gone," Miss B said. "Fuckin' hell."

"Nooooooo!" I said with what was left of my voice. I had been dealing with bronchitis for about a month and it wasn't going anywhere anytime soon. Ice cream was the only thing that soothed my throat.

Miss B opened a box of chicken nuggets and it was like she'd gone to heaven.

"Oh, hell yeah, come to mama, lil' chicks."

I dug my good hand into the vegetables like a love-struck woman, thinking that the vitamins would heal me. My left hand still felt kooky after the kitchen mishap. It still hurt enough that I avoided using it. I started placing carrots (25 to be exact) down my pants. Did carrots have fiber?

Miss B said, "Runnin' a train huh?"

"Running a train?"

I hadn't been on a train before. I also hadn't stolen anything before prison. I had to admit it felt good. The adrenaline sparked up my veins. It felt similar to striking a million-dollar deal abroad. The excitement swelling in the chest, the rise of oxytocin, the love drug. I had to get my kicks somewhere.

Miss B tossed a considerable supply of nuggets into a lard-covered pan, and piled them into her trap, as did I. They were hot as hell, but we continued our dark poultry binge. (I turned the lights off because of my migraine.) Steam smoked our mouths like dragons.

It was just after the 10 a.m. count (which took place on weekends). We had plenty of time before the next formal count at 4 p.m. Basically, if a con wanted to launch any type of shady business, it needed to happen between 10 a.m. and 4 p.m. It was also visitation, so most people were engaged in some form of chatter, including the guards. Or so we thought.

Mr. Clark heaved open the kitchen door. The one time I thanked God for my migraines. Miss B had always told me that we had to abide by the rules… while staff was looking. And thank God Mr. Clark couldn't see in the dark. He had a lot of powers, but being a cat wasn't one of them. He was not nocturnal. He could not see in the dark.

Miss B stashed the last nugget in her waistband; she couldn't let it go, although it was sizzling hot. I definitely didn't want him to see what I had down my pants: enough orange to paint a sunset.

Mr. Clark flipped on the lights. "I don't buy this friendship," he said as he leaned on the steel countertop.

Miss B could hardly talk, "Really?" Her eyes watered. I could barely talk, either (bronchitis).

"You don't think I know that everyone is working an angle?"

"Really?" Miss B said with an indifferent tone. She adjusted her pants slightly.

"It will put you behind the fence, you know."

"What," I said softly.

"Stealing food."

"What do you think we are? Animals?" I said. I had a pretty good poker face.

He hopped up on the counter and made himself comfortable. Miss B looked as though she had to urinate. She held her legs together and was standing kind of wonky. She kept adjusting her stance. I was uncomfortable for her.

"When you see inmates as anything but a person, there's a problem," Mr. Clark said. "You don't want to send that animal out into the world."

Miss B was unusually quiet. Mr. Clark picked up on it.

"You okay?"

"Don't pay me no mind."

"That's my job."

Miss B said, "What?"

"Paying you mind." He paused his dialogue.

"Oh, right. Right," Miss B said.

"Someone has been popping the lock on the freezer," Mr. Clark crossed his arms. "They've been getting their lips wet with ice cream."

Miss B said, "That's sad, Mr. Clark. Whoever done that." Her brow beaded with sweat.

"Stolen food will put you behind the fence. How many times have you been shipped to county, Miss B? We going on five now?"

"Four, sir." She fanned her shirt.

"If you work us, we'll work you," Mr. Clark said. With that, he got up and left.

Miss B opened her waistband, the nugget dropped onto the floor. She checked over her stomach. It looked like the nugget had caused third-degree burns. I rubbed some butter on it. It wasn't as if she could skip down to medical. There was only so much Tylenol could do. She still had a hole in her stomach. Scarred by a nugget.

"Pass it to me," Miss B said. She shoved the nugget into her mouth.

Mr. Clark opened the door again, hoping to catch the thieves in the act.

Miss B swallowed the evidence, "Forget somethin'?"

"Don't steal food," he said.

Chapter 7

A Field Guide to Surviving Prison II

Disobey Direct Orders

The rumor mill started. It happened when people saw that a con was semi-successful, and Miss B and I weren't slowing down. The funny thing about rumors was that it was sort of like free marketing. People talking shit turned our little enterprise into a brand with a lucrative financial forecast.

We had stolen vegetables, snacks and commissary hidden all over the camp. The great thing about preservative-packed food and non-organic produce was that it lasted. Have you ever left a genetically modified apple to age on the counter? It lasts for months! Most of our product was lodged in the ceiling panels where Miss B washed dishes, although it turned out that we had to re-locate it. When reading the kitchen schedule one week, we realized that our names weren't on it.

"What we fired for?" Miss B said.

"For throwing out food, stealing eggs and whatever else," Camilla retorted. "Don't look at me, someone saw you."

Mr. Clark told me that cons tattled on me left, right and center. It was mostly food-oriented:

"*They* say Sallon be tossin' food," con No. 1 said.

"*They* say Sallon is joined with Isis," one of Miss Kelly's rats said.

"*They* say Sallon gave away free bacon," con No. 2 said.

"*They* say Sallon gave away free eggs," con No. 3 said.

Mr. Clark responded by asking who *they* were. Not many cons would elaborate. He responded by stating that he "wasn't anyone's pit bull," which meant that he wasn't going to sic anyone without evidence.

However, two witnesses saw me dump the "perfectly fine" cockroach-infested pancake mix, and one witness (cough, cough, Blaze) saw me making eggs for a con. Ha!

Mr. Clark saw the petty crimes as enough evidence to work me into an orderly position, the lowest-paying job. The witnesses were credible after all.

*   *   *

USA VS MINA SALLON — DETROIT, MI — APRIL 2007 — 5 PM

She said, "these witnesses came before you and they told you essentially the same thing, and that is that Mina Sallon told them that the equipment was going to Iraq. She knew about the embargo and she was trying to ship it to a third country to hide the fact that it was going to Iraq."

1   "Ambrose Tiller, from Texas, gave Mina a 'cease and desist order' and said that he couldn't help her any longer because the equipment was bound by customs, that it has a ciphering algorithm in it that's bound by export control laws."

2   "Conner Grigoryan, the shipper from England, said that Mina first told him that the shipment was going to Turkey. This changed when they met at a teahouse with Sami Al-Mufti, when Mina overheard that the GSM equipment was going to Iraq."

3   "Mina told the same basic story to her former best friend Dina. She told her that over the course of conversation, in London, that she was shipping telecommunications equipment to Iraq."

4   "No name was defendant Mina Sallon's former fiancé. You will recall that he testified he was working with Sami at LIE, and that LIE had an office in Baghdad. He said that Mina sent shipments to the Ministry of Communications in Baghdad. You know that the shipment didn't go to Turkey, it went to Iraq."

In this moment I felt as though a bullet was shot straight into my chest. I became the center of it all, the mastermind so to speak. Truly, I was some pawn in an international game of chess, headed by Sami Al-Mufti. But they weren't about to reveal classified information in court, especially when it involved a CIA asset.

USA VS MINA SALLON — DETROIT, MI — APRIL 2007 — 5:10 PM

She said, "Now you may ask yourself, why isn't Sami Al-Mufti on trial too? Sami is a coconspirator. Well, the Judge will instruct you that your focus should be on the defendants. And the fact that other coconspirators aren't on trial doesn't matter. The export laws involved in this case apply to U.S. persons, and he's not. He's a foreigner. That's why he's not here."

When my brother heard this synopsis of witness testimonies, and why Sami wasn't to take any blame, his mouth was agape. He said it was like someone saying, "I'm going to dump this trash on you; dig yourself out."

I felt as if everyone was against me, including my fiancé. Of course, the jury would have thought that I bent for No name and Sami's company. But that's just what the prosecution did. Distorted information. Had I sent boxes to Iraq in the scope of my life? Yes, the Oil-for-Food program allowed it. And, because of the embargo, I dotted all of my i's and crossed all of my t's. Did I send tele-communications equipment to Iraq? No, I did not. The General had told my dad that sometimes civilians were used in military operations without their knowledge. And I believed this is exactly what this was. I was a fucking scape-goat.

She said, "Now what about the defendant's motive? What would make Ms. Sallon try to ship millions of dollars of telecommunications equipment to Iraq at this time on the eve of war with the United States? What would drive some-one to do that? Greed. Greed for money, but greed for success, too."

*   *   *

"Here comes trouble," Blaze said as Miss B and I made our way to visitation.

"I don't address you," Miss B said. "Don't address us."

Nobody was in the hallway, apart from Blaze, and I wondered why.

"There's going to be a shake down," Miss B said. About twice a month the guards would search the entire camp for contraband. The smart cookies had most of their stuff crammed in the cracks: in the ceiling, in the bathroom wall, or in a carved-out book. The dumb buckets got caught and were sent to the hole, or behind the fence.

Miss B made a habit of dropping me off at visitation, as no one visited her. Not once. Not ever.

"Don't give 'em up," Miss B whispered to me.

"What up?"

"The carrots, duh."

My mom visited me today and brought me more cash. She was basically our venture capitalist. And I promised her a return on her investment. She looked weird when she sat down, like a screw was loose. Her hair was all over the place, and her coat was wrinkled.

"What's going on?" I said.

"Did you get the magazines?"

My mom had been sending me cash in magazines. She hid it in various places: between pages that she had glued together, or in the perfume flap. She was funny, that mother of mine. She always gave hints as to where she stashed the goods via letters. She said:

> *Am sending 3 magazines to pass the time. Reader's Digest has lots of interesting stuff buried inside, check out the joke section! I haven't read the other magazines but one article stood out, "The Revolutionary Way to Lose Weight Fast." NOT. Have you smelled J'adore? Wow! Take time to read what I've sent and digest them. Also sending picture of different types of orchids with sayings. Perhaps, cut them out and paste them somewhere as a reminder. Well, at any rate, I send them with love and from my heart to my baby daughter. – Love, mom.*

"You don't need to spell it out," I said. "Truly."

"Well, I don't know honey. How am I supposed to know? Just remember what put you away, Mina."

The visitation orderly caught my attention. She was a homely girl with stringy, brown hair. Her face was swollen and bruised. I had never seen her before, and I wondered why. She looked like a squirrel, with those puffy cheeks, and the way she moved … scurrying about along the perimeter of the room, emptying trash bins ever so quietly. No one paid attention to her.

"Are you listening, Mina?"

"I know, I know, I fucked up," I said. "Do we have to dwell on it?"

"No," my mother said. When she was short, I knew there was a problem.

"What?" I said, "What? Did greed put me away?"

My mother was also putting money on Miss B's books now. She was frequenting multiple Western Unions at least once a week for us. She made up bogus names and return addresses. You better bet those names were on our charts/visitation lists: Agatha Connors from Detroit, June Rogers from Flint, and Eva Smith from Lapeer.

"Sometimes you get too caught up," my mother said.

She was right. Greed played a part in my eventual lockup. I sometimes put my hands in too many baskets and lost sight of intricacies. But this was too easy.

*   *   *

USA VS MINA SALLON — DETROIT, MI — APRIL 2007 — 5:06 PM
She said, "I think you were greedy, and I think you let your greed get the best of you. You wanted to excel in the international market, and you didn't care what came your way. You were going to take chances. You were going to take risks."

*   *   *

Who didn't take risks in business? The most profitable businesses took risks. The visit ended with my mother saying, "Every dollar I make goes to you."

I headed to the restroom to collect the cash my mother had left in the usual drop spot, the trash can. The squirrel was emptying the trash as I entered.

"What's your name?" I asked.

"Charlie," she said. She could barely open her mouth.

Charlie was having difficulty with her medical issues (like the rest of us). She did not have any priors to prison four years earlier. She was a sweet girl and I felt bad for her. She was about to get her uterus removed; she was only 38, by the way. And something was fucked up with her kidneys. She had to get stints put in.

But the swollen face was due to her wisdom teeth being removed (by interns at a university). She said they laughed as they read her chart, which Charlie said was upside down. The also missed her vein three times while trying to administer anesthesia, until one of the interns finally said, "I think I better go get somebody." That's the care inmates received.

Her face was so enlarged; she said it tripled in size. Her dental plan began at another prison, behind the fence (where they *really* didn't care about inmates). After waiting two years, in and out of pain (and through being transferred to Kentucky), she finally got some relief, or so she thought. She now had a hell of an infection and was extremely nauseous.

"Let me help you with the trash," I said.

I offered her a position in our company and told her I'd pay her $50 a month, which was a great sum for her. She had a husband and an 11-year-old daughter somewhere and $50 would help them. She was happy with that. All she had to do was collect trash at visitation.

The positions in our company: Charlie was Chief Operating Officer (COO) handling the day-to-day tasks. I was the Chief Executive Officer (CEO), in charge of acquiring funds. And Miss B was the Chief Financial Officer (CFO), charged with multiplying my investment.

*   *   *

Anything I gave Miss B, she turned. I gave her $100 and she came out with $300. She was a hustler. One of her ventures was built solely on shoes. She kept track of when cons were to be released and bought out their stinky foot-wear. She then cleaned and sold said shoes for half the price that commissary was selling them for.

Mr. Clark once found seven to eight pairs under Miss B's bed.

He said, "These your shoes?"

"No. These are Lucia's shoes. These are Blaze's shoes…"

"…What are you doing with other people's shoes?"

"Cleaning them."

"Cleaning them," he said.

"Cleaning them."

Miss B also noticed with her sharp eyes that there wasn't a lock on the door in the basement. There also wasn't an alarm, which made it the perfect spot for a drop. It was another profitable enterprise.

We had a nice little system set up. My mother would pick up a list of goods: L'Oréal lipstick, Girl Scout cookies, lavender oil, Pureology shampoo, ciga-rettes … whatever cons ached for. Usually, things that reminded them of home. My mom then mailed the box of items to Miss B's friend, Shelly, in Kentucky (along with a drop-off fee). Shelly would then drive up for visitation on a week-end and drop the package at the basement door. Our little squirrel (the COO) in charge of daily operations would collect it for us.

One time, I found Miss B counting $100 bills in her bunk, like it was a reg-ular Saturday. "Where did you get that?" I said.

"Visitation baby, the families," she said. We collected cash on visitation days and the products were promised to the cons in one week's time.

Miss B once told me, "I don't have time to think about being locked up with you as a friend." We kept ourselves busy.

*   *   *

I bunkered down for the night after the 9 p.m. count. I was hungry but didn't want commissary or vending machine garbage. Plus, I didn't keep my goodies in my room because of the rats. I would kill for a shawarma with extra pickles and hummus, the type of sandwich that dripped deliciousness. Maybe my mom could mail one in a Styrofoam cooler with ice. I'd look into it. I didn't want to dwell on my stomach, as I usually did. Plus, if I slept now… the closer I'd be to breakfast. Sleeping was a time machine to food. Also, I didn't want to be tired in the morning. I was grouchy when I was tired. And if I was grouchy, my mother (who was set to visit) would be short with me, and I couldn't take that. Seeing her upset killed me.

I thought about things that would solve my problems, like winning the lottery. I often fantasized about this. If I could just win a million, I'd be back to where I started.

I thought of masturbating. That usually put me straight to sleep, but I hated flicking the bean with Miss Kelly in the room. It really destroyed the vibe.

I also reformulated my 2002 deal with Sami in my head. I envisioned circumstances that kept me out of prison. Like sending the telecommunications equipment myself at a post office in the UK. The postman would say things like, "To Turkey, then?" and I'd say, "Bloody brilliant." Circumstances that left me with big sums in my bank account.

I counted the acoustic ceiling tiles: 1, 2, 3, 4, 5, 6, 7, 8, 9…109…and at about 10 p.m., Rachel marched into our room with an agenda. I faced the floor with terror. She opened my cooler and discovered a whole lot of orange.

"Narc," I said to Miss Kelly.

Rachel grabbed my arm and led me straight to Mr. Clark.

*   *   *

Miss B stood near Mr. Clark's window and peeked in, every now and again. Mr. Clark had my cooler in hand. He held up a photo of Micah's plane (that he had sent me), the Cessna RG. Micah wrote: *to fly you home ;)*

"This is why people hate you," he said.

"People hate me?"

"Half of these inmates can't afford a soup at commissary, and you're rolling around with a plane in your back pocket."

He held up the 25 carrots.

"Making a carrot cake?"

"What, am I on trial?"

"What does a person need 25 carrots for?"

"Knowing there is food near me, I don't know … relaxes me."

He plopped the carrots on his desk, "Why, Sallon, just why?"

"I'm going to eat well, and I'll do what I have to do!"

"You disobeyed a direct order," he said. "Don't steal food."

I was silenced.

"Are you guilty of stealing carrots, Sallon? Answer the question."

*   *   *

USA VS MINA SALLON — DETROIT, MI — APRIL 2007 — 5:10 PM

"I'd like to speak with an Armenian priest before any further questions," Conner Grigoryan said on the stand. Why he wanted to speak to a priest I'd never know. Grigoryan was the smoking gun. The witness that cast doubt toward the jury. He worked for a shipping company in the UK. The one that shipped *the equipment*. We had a meeting with Sami at a swanky hotel in the UK, one that had a teahouse. One of those places that served three-tiered silver platters of tiny cucumber sandwiches and a selection of teas that would make the Mad Hatter envious. And it was this little meeting that sent me down the rabbit hole.

In the course of the meeting, Sami organized the shipment. According to Grigoryan, Sami related that the package was going through Syria as a transshipment point into Iraq, and that the deal was UN-approved. I heard no such thing. The prosecutor said that I was deliberately ignorant.

Turning to the jury, *She* said, "Let me give you an analogy that someone gave me to explain deliberate ignorance. Someone comes to you with a bag and says, 'Hey, take this bag of cocaine and deliver it to the man on the street corner.' You say, 'I can't do that. That would be illegal.' And so, the person immediately says to you, 'Let me give you this bag of candy. Would you deliver it to the man on the street corner?' And you say, 'Okay, I'm not going to look in the bag. I'll deliver it.' That's deliberate ignorance. You can't avoid criminal responsibility by ignoring the obvious. And you can't see a high probability of equipment going to Iraq and bury your head in the sand and pretend it's not happening."

This is the part where everything blew up. *She* said, "Answer the question, Mr. Grigoryan."

Grigoryan said, "Yes, Mina was there."

She said, "So, what you're saying is that Mina Sallon was at the teahouse during the course of your conversation with Sami Al-Mufti, and she clearly knew where the equipment was going?"

Loren Monday said, "Objection, your honor, this is a leading question."

Judge Battaglia said, "Overruled. Restate the question."

She said, "Could Mina Sallon have heard where the equipment was destined?"

Grigoryan said, "Yes, she could have heard the destination."

She could have heard the destination killed me.

I watched as the court reporter typed it all up.

*   *   *

"I'm going to have to write you up," Mr. Clark said. He wrote an Incident Report as I lamented. If a con collected enough reports, it meant more time, fewer privileges and multiple officers' eyes on your back.

"My mom is coming to visit," I said. "All the way from Michigan."

"You know what the consequences are. Don't complain if you know what the consequences are."

Miss B weaseled her way into the room.

Mr. Clark said, "Sorry, did someone invite you in?"

"Mr. Clark, Sallon didn't mean to disrespect you or anyone else. It just sort of happened. She's been backed up. Real backed up." She sat down.

Mr. Clark looked at Miss B like she was nuts.

"Sallon, she's slow," she continued. "I think she's slow."

I looked at Miss B like she was nuts.

Mr. Clark opened my file and took out a program review. In it was a former response sumSallon of my personal character. He read it aloud:

"Mina Sallon has behaviors indicative of positive personal character, she does regular volunteer work (not court ordered), she has evidence of spirituality (she examines actions to see if they reflect her values), she fulfills financial obligations (she pays her restitution) and provides assistance to strangers without the expectation of rewards."

*   *   *

USA VS MINA SALLON — DETROIT, MI — APRIL 2007 — 5:16 PM

She said, "The court has reviewed the letters, and I see that others view you as a good woman, Ms. Sallon. They're probably quite surprised by this violation. But they say, and I have no reason to disbelieve, that you have been a person who helps others in the community. I also do not disbelieve that you're a smart person, and that you're well-educated and you have a master's degree. However, I suppose that in a sense it's not a positive thing here, because being as smart as I believe you are (as your grades and degrees show), you should have at least paused before you got involved in this transaction."

I should have paused before I did a lot of things.

*   *   *

Mr. Clark looked at me. "I wrote up this character report just last year."

"Sounds just about right," I said.

"I want you to leave prison better, not bitter," he said. "Do you think you can do that?"

"Yes." I'd be leaving all right. I'd walk straight off the grounds and hitch a ride to Mexico. This was bullshit. Who in the hell got in trouble for eating fucking carrots? "Don't leave bitter," he said. I'd leave right now if I had the opportunity and I'd shove the incident report straight up his ass.

Mr. Clark ripped up the Incident Report. He pointed at me.

"Mind your damn business. Don't disrespect anybody. Do your time. And don't feed the animals; they'll associate you with food."

Destroy Property

On a Saturday, Miss B told me that I was "a full-time job." She almost shouted it, to be heard over the dryers. Her new job assignment was in the laundry room, which was both pristine and disorderly. The janitorial cons kept it up with cleaning products. But there were dirty emerald uniforms everywhere. The air also smelled like sweat, more sweat and bleach. Miss Kelly was head of the cleanup crew, and she was revered among her subservient clan. She looked like her soul more than ever on this day: vacant. She mopped the floor while mean muggin' everyone.

We spent most of our time in the laundry room, scrubbing uniforms, washing uniforms and folding uniforms. I volunteered to illustrate more of my "positive personal character."

A memorandum was tacked to the wall: WASHING CLOTHES AFTER HOURS IS OVER. Miss B, Charlie and I had been washing clothes after hours. At least that's what we said we were doing when a corrections officer caught Miss B and I downstairs.

Laundry was in the basement, closer to our drop site. So, there was one pro in a long reel of cons. It was cool, so a ton of inmates scurried in and out of the place. It was home to the Mexican gang (including Lucia). Additionally, it was the comfy abode to a surplus of roaches and mice. I sent out another Inmate Request to Staff regarding the pests. The response was:

> *The safety department has been made aware of this issue and is addressing it. Bait stations have been placed in strategic areas of the unit. This concentrated effort of baiting and trapping rodents will continue as long as necessary. To assist with this process, it is imperative room sanitation is at best. The staff regards sanitation and safety as priorities and takes every precaution to ensure living conditions are maintained at appropriate and safe levels – Warden*

The bait stations were placed in *such* strategic locations that they couldn't be seen. Ha! I couldn't believe that the warden had actually signed it.

"If I were to leave, what do you think would be the ideal time?"

Miss B tapped on her Bible.

"Don't start," I said.

Miss B opened the Bible. Inside was a complete log of everyone and everything inside of the prison. Some entries were two years old. There were guard profiles and habits, inmate profiles and habits, and schedules. You name it and it was in there. I opened up a page on Miss Kelly:

> *Miss Kelly (60s). White hair. Bitch is from Boston, South side. Rumor is she's a Criminal Lawyer? Ponzi scheme got her inside. Fraud. Starts shit 4 shits and giggles. Turns friend on friend. Smart as hell. Wicked. Racist. Does laundry at 3 on Saturdays. Naps at 2. What she want? Pack of white followers. Bitch wants chaos.*

Miss B pointed to Sunday. There were nine hours in between counts on Sunday. That would be the day I'd sneak out. No one would miss me. We had probably folded our 100th green uniform when I said, "I'm going to Mexico."

"Know anyone there?" Miss B said as she folded industriously. She was a hard worker and I loved her for it. And she always went along with my ideas. She was a positive support system. I think she knew that I'd talk myself out of it. But I wasn't going to this time. No, I wasn't going to this time.

"Not yet," I replied.

"Let me shake some trees."

About an hour later, Miss B talked Lucia into sneaking me out with the laundry. A couple miles down the street at a place called "Bluegrass Burritos," one of her loco Mexican cousins would meet me and wheel me off to Mexico in his sedan. I wondered if we could order burritos before we headed south of the border. There would be over 24 hours to kill.

The whole thing would cost less than $1,000. Lucia said, "You don't need nothing. No passport; nothing. My family? No one fucks with them. You're on your own once he drops you."

Lucia also wanted assurances that our business (in my absence) would only sell to the white and black cars. Next Sunday. Just like that, the plan was hatched. It was on.

"Maybe I will have a chance to have kids," I said.

"I pray you will," Miss B said. "Little half-Arab, half-Spanish ones. I'm going to give your ass more time, too."

"To have kids?"

"To peace out, dumdum. I'm not a magician."

"How's that?"

"You know how most house fires start?"

*   *   *

Miss B was a pyromaniac. She loved starting fires and she was obsessed. She told me that producing one starting point (of a fire) guaranteed that insurance covered the damages. Multiple starting points equaled insurance fraud. Not that she cared in this instance. But the fewer questions, the better.

On the Sunday of my departure, in the laundry room at 11 am, I ate what I thought would be my last burger. When I got out, I was going to change my eating habits. I wanted to limit red meat. Unless, in fact, Lucia's loco cousin stopped for burritos. Steak burritos were my jam. In that case, my diet would start on Monday.

"I'm a new woman," I said to Miss B.

"I believe that," she said, handing me around $200.

"I couldn't," I said.

"Buy me a margarita," she said.

I had already paid Lucia her $1,000 fee, sending my books back to zero. Well, now I was at $200. I didn't have a plan once I got to Mexico, but I spoke some Spanish and I had a master's degree in International Marketing Management. That would cover it, I thought.

Soon, Lucia would be covering me. Some of the laundry was outsourced. A company called Keep it Clean picked it up every Sunday. Lucia knew the driver. She would roll a laundry cart up the ramp (complete with me in it, covered by uniforms) and into the truck. Said truck would roll away and make a routine rest stop at Bluegrass Burritos. Driver would open up the back door, I'd shake hands with Lucia's loco cousin, and I'd be halfway to Mexico before the guards knew I was missing.

Miss B would light a match in one of the dryers approximately eight hours after my departure, right before count time. This would create more of a stir. The commotion would give me more time.

I instructed Miss B to send a letter to my mother with a parrot on it. That she'd know what it meant. My mother loved to travel, "experiencing different cultures," she called it. She went to Cancun with Isabel one year and the two of them had a blast posing with parrots. A picture from the front, two from the back, some shots with cabana boys they didn't even know. Basically, they were really into it. They were also very liquored up and probably pissed off a red bird named Linda. The beautiful bird took a chunk out of my mom's arm. The scar is still there.

"How the fuck am I going to draw a parrot?" Miss B said.

"It's not rocket science."

"Let me level with you. My art is low-key, bad."

"So, don't send the parrot. I'll figure it out."

"I got you."

"What are you doing?" Rachel said from the door.

"Washing clothes," Miss B said.

Rachel pointed to the memorandum: WASHING CLOTHES AFTER HOURS IS OVER.

"Get out, inmates."

On our way out of the laundry room, Miss Kelly was engaged in conversation with Lucia, which was fishy because they rolled in different cars. Miss Kelly had a broom in hand. Lucia had a blank expression. Both stopped talking when Miss B and I walked by. I guess Rachel saved my ass. But I lost the money. And I lost the burritos.

*   *   *

I headed to the call center, which included blue phone booths in close proximity, long lines (like Disneyland), and cataloging of all conversations. A little bit of trivia: My brokering business with Micah actually commenced with the calling-card business. The ones you scratched off for a penny a minute. I think my balance was five minutes.

I entered a booth and dialed my mom. There was no answer. I dialed again.

"Back of the line, inmate," Rachel said.

"But…"

"Back of the line!"

I waited in the line again for another hour. I dialed.

"You have a collect call from an inmate at a Kentucky Federal Prison. Do you accept the charges?"

"Yes," my mom said.

"Mom, have you heard from Dad?"

"Focus on the day-to-day, honey."

"I'm worried. Is it too much to ask?"

"I divorced the man. I don't have his itinerary."

"I want to freeze my eggs," I said. "I need ten grand."

Rachel gave me a look.

"This is getting to be a bit much, honey."

"I'm in prison. Sorry, how is it a bit much for *you*?"

"We're all in prison. Me, your father and Micah. Micah is hurting, Mina. I can't tell you how often he's said that he wishes he was in your position, as I do."

"Is this another guilt trip?"

"When you decide to talk to him, instead of 'When am I getting out,' how about 'I love you, I miss you, thank you keep fighting,' or even 'How are you?'"

"Can you just help me?"

"No, Mina, I will not send you ten grand."

"Fuck you!"

I hung up the phone. I wish I hadn't, but I did. My mother referred to me as "nasty," at this time. I was. I was a nasty piece of work.

*   *   *

USA VS MINA SALLON — DETROIT, MI — APRIL 2007 — 5:18 PM

She said, "I am very sympathetic to her position, that as a 36-year-old woman who wants marriage and children, we are asking for a very severe sentence for her. But I don't think we can treat offenders differently because of their age or gender."

*   *   *

In those days, I cut off people like it was nothing. Like my problems were more important that theirs. Nonetheless, the letters still came:

> **April 14th, 2010:** *Diva, where are you? Take a deep breath. Exhale. Do it again 8-10 times. Relax. This Kelly woman and Rachel can do nothing unless you confirm it. I'm going to call them "She." She torments you.   Why? Because YOU LET HER! Tell yourself that she doesn't exist. Say NOTHING. DO NOTHING. And watch the dance, the "look at me dance." No one is looking. You thinking of her, and focusing your upset on her, you inadvertently send her energy. You are FEEDING HER. Should she be eating like a princess? Heck, no! She is laying a trap and baiting you. You WIN if you do not play. Have I shaken the cobwebs out of you? – Isabel Baker*

Rachel had heard that I wanted to freeze my eggs. She then proceeded to sell the story to some newspaper. My mother saw the article:

> *Convicted felon, Mina Sallon, wishes to freeze her eggs. Sallon was convicted of breaking a U.S. trade embargo with Iraq, a 9.5-million-dollar deal. She was sentenced to 6 years in a Federal prison.*

How fucking embarrassing.

> **April 18th, 2010:** *Mina, I spoke to MacCann. She said that she would certainly be willing to look into any problems of harassment or the like, but she is not proposing to agree to reducing your sentence or release you on bond.*
>
> *Do you really want to ask her to communicate with the prison regarding the problems you are having with some of your fellow inmates, or with health services? I don't think you want to hear my advice right now. I also think you know what it is. I want to see you manage the situation better, and am sure you can. – Monday*

Whatever.

> **April 23rd, 2010:** *How are you? Sorry it has taken a while to get back to you, but I had a number of things to attend to. Not sure if your mother told you, but Dina popped back into my life. She introduced me to a Chinese businessman, and a US businessman who informed me that he worked with the United Nations and the CIA. He said something like, 'Whenever people needed*

advocacy, they contacted him.' I told him about your case and asked if he could help in some way. He said, "I help the CIA government to government, not individual cases." Anyhow, about a month later I kept getting calls from the US man, very aggressive, which claimed he couldn't get a hold of Dina and needed me to call her. I was like NO! What does your mother say? Fool me once, shame on me… Fool me twice? Anyhow, you know the rest.

I was also trying to find further information regarding legal aspects of me writing your book through a friend's entertainment lawyer. Have you heard of the Son of Sam law? Something you should research. Basically, criminals can't profit from their sentences and crimes. Anyhow, we'll get it done, some way, somehow. I promise! People need to hear your story! Hope you're well friend, I miss you. – Abida.

Why did people insist on writing when there wasn't solid news?

April 25th, 2010: *Dear honorable (insert name here):*

I am writing to request your assistance in having new mitigating information related to the prosecution of Michigan resident, Mina Sallon. I request a 30-minute meeting to discuss the sensitive aspects of this matter.

While I have served over 30 years with the U.S. ARMY, the majority of the time with U.S. ARMY counterintelligence, I am writing as a private citizen. Ms. Sallon's case was brought to my attention in 2008 by Ms. Sallon's father, Mansur Sallon. Mansur had served as one of my interpreters when I was the Director of the Strategic Counterintelligence Directorate, Baghdad, Iraq.

In brief, when Ms. Sallon was working as an international broker, she became involved in a transaction to ship used telecommunications equipment for what she believed was a project in Turkey. It turns out, and a CIA asset has confirmed, the shipment was actually destined for Baghdad for a CIA project. Ms. Sallon was convicted for shipping the equipment to Iraq. Had Ms. Sallon known the equipment was being shipped to Iraq, I've been informed that she could have received State Department approval with a two-page form.

More troubling to me, is that the government may have known the project Ms. Sallon was supporting might have been sponsored by the CIA and that this information was not made available during discovery and was not known to the defense and jury during the trial.

I would ask your assistance in reviewing this case. Sincerely, The General

This was the letter the General sent me. He was slipping it under the doors of Washington. He was a great advocate, the General, until someone from higher up told him to stand down. Everything was swept under the rug. Everything.

The General was doing my dad's work. I still hadn't heard from my father, but I knew he was working hard to get me out. He was the type of person who would only contact me to tell me that I was free. He'd say something like, "I'm coming to get you, my little baklava. It's over."

April 29th, 2010: *Mina, I will always refer to you as my sweet daughter, a blessing from God. I am deeply saddened by the language you use when referencing me. The hatred is very apparent right now. Just so you know, no matter what you say or how you feel about me, you will ALWAYS be my daughter. I realize that this sentence is truly wrong, unfair, a grave injustice. But, we are up against an entire government. However, there are events in all lives that are unfair — death, for instance, is unfair. I miss my mom—I miss laughing out loud with her when selecting a card for an occasion. Whenever there is news, I pick up the phone to call her, then put it back down. I miss that I can't call her. I miss being called my late husband's "bride." I even miss his little habits that once made me angry. I miss his big hugs and his gentle touch. You keep saying, "They are taking away my thirties." In reality, they have taken years from everyone in the family. "They" would revel in the fact that "they" have taken our family savings, and that "they" caused a rift in our loving and close family. If we give in, "they" win. If we quit, our family continues to divide. I will not give up, not ever. We can regain our wealth, and independence, but we have to remain united. We are all suffering, but this isn't cancer, we aren't dying—I hurt too. – Love, mom.*

I had to give it to my mother. She always remained positive. She always supported me on the daily. She always put my needs before hers. I needed to grow my gratitude for her, that was for certain.

Create a Disturbance

Cons were smoking cigarettes we had smuggled in all over the prison. In the library, smoke billowed and cons were euphoric. In the kitchen, the clamoring of dishes paused and cons were euphoric. In the yard, voices were quieted, and cons were euphoric.

In the bus stop, there was a haze that spread throughout the room. It felt like the walls of the prison didn't exist anymore, like I was in a pasture somewhere warm, like the sun was shining on my face and I didn't have any obligations that day. It kind of felt like I was free.

"Look under my bed," Miss B said as she popped caramels into her mouth. She had more than 20 pairs of shoes under there.

"Hoarder," I replied.

"This camp off the chain, Sallon. Most comfortable I've ever been."

"Where did three years go?" I said.

"You make people feel free, Detroit."

Chapter 8

OPEN SEASON

My new nickname was the Robin Hood of Kentucky. My stock value was at an all-time high with the inmates. The business Miss B and I had created was a well-oiled machine. People respected us.

Miss B said, "We have a whole garden in our coolers."

I said, "Don't wake me up. I'm on vacation. Go get me some of the coffee that the staff drinks." If I wanted a nap, I used her bunk in the bus stop. I vacated Miss Kelly's room whenever I could.

"Detroit, you aren't real."

"In my real life, I got vacation."

The truth was that I didn't remember life before prison. Any thoughts of the outside world and my goals (family and children) I had purged from my head, like pulling out a decaying tooth. Daydreams didn't belong in my skull anymore.

The previous night I had a night terror. I dreamed of my sentencing again. The one where I knew the verdict before the gavel pummeled the bench. The one where my family and I all stood knee-deep in murky water, and my mother fell into the dark cesspool. Even after my father had said that our family "would never drown." No one turned around in the court to help my mother and I couldn't move my neck. I couldn't stand hearing my mother's guttural wail, the one that stayed with me and sent shivers up my back.

In this version, something was different, though. There was a dense fog billowing in the room, like a heavy mask that couldn't be removed. A death mask. I was conscious that there were people in the room, even though I couldn't move my head or see them. They were so silent, as silent as when you have sound-canceling earphones on. It made me tense. I was stiff when I woke up and carried the nightmare with me throughout the day. I was loyal to it.

"You a bad motha' fucka, Detroit," Miss B said as she handed me a coffee. Miss B's positive affirmations usually made me feel like I could take on the world. But I couldn't shake the haunting vibe of my nightmare.

"When's the drop?" Trina said.

"Don't trip. Patience is a virtue" Miss B said.

"Where is the drop?" I asked Miss B.

Miss B went to find Charlie, who was supposed to be at the drop location in the basement at exactly 2 p.m. It was now 3 p.m. Charlie was really starting to annoy me. She was still recovering from her surgeries and had asked if I would fill her Downy bottle at the ice machine around 1 p.m. Usually I didn't mind because I had to pass the bus stop (where Miss B was) and I could poke my head in, like today. It was just around the corner on the same floor as us. I tried to be a good bunkie by helping with her face, which was still rather large, by the way. She had a follow-up surgery on her teeth (a bunch of teeth were pulled) and it seemed as though she got an infection this time as well. They didn't give her antibiotics. The girl had bad luck. But she never complained. She was the type of person who made the most of things. Anyway, I went back to Miss Kelly's room to give her the ice and she was nowhere to be found.

An alarm blared. Fucking hell, what was it this time? Cons made their way down the stairwell and into the yard, as guards yelled directions:

"Single file ladies, don't shove!"

We stood in the yard (in our units), as guards counted us. It was February and the temperature was mild, although the wind tussled my hair. Cons chatted in their units. Miss Kelly looked chipper and I wholeheartedly questioned it.

"Miss Kelly has the drop," Miss B whispered as she made her way to her unit.

"What the fuck?"

"Our girl was late," Miss B said when we were allowed back inside. Not only that, but they fixed the alarm at our drop site. It was the one thing they decided to fix in a mound of broken shit.

"Not our girl anymore," I said. "We have to set the bar high."

Miss B said, "Put that bar down baby, before you trip over it."

Blaze swung by to relate that Miss Kelly wanted to chat. Of course, she did.

"When the going gets tough, the tough get going," Blaze said. She also asked if I'd put money on her account to ring her kid.

"Yes, I can do that," I said. Her boss had my box. Of course, I'd do it and I'm sure there would be a few things I'd need to add on that "to do" list for Miss Kelly. Miss B and I would have been in Mr. Clark's office, otherwise.

Blaze and I were in a good place because I had written up a document to give her aunt and uncle power of attorney. Her kid was in their hands now. I figured I might as well help anyone that I could while I was knee-deep in this mess. My father would have been proud. He was the most charitable man I knew.

Another story (my mom related to me) was when The General asked why my dad was in Iraq. He said something to the effect of, "I need to free innocent people because I can't free my daughter." To know that people were freed because I went to prison made me feel a bit better about my current address.

*   *   *

USA VS MINA SALLON — DETROIT, MI — APRIL 2007 — 5:20 PM
She said, "There are some other questions that Sallon's lawyer raised. Monday said that if Sallon were guilty, why would she have complained to customs officials when they stopped the shipment? Why would the Sallon family write to congressmen? What if Curve Tech just went away quietly and never inquired about their goods again? Wouldn't it look even worse? Maybe that's why. Or maybe they thought they could outsmart everybody. Micah has a PhD and Mina has a master's degree in international business. Maybe they just thought they could outsmart everybody."

*   *   *

Miss Kelly said, "I have something of yours. Your package." Miss Kelly's room was almost lightless around this time. Shadows lined her face like a noir film. Blaze was high as a kite, as usual. Miss Kelly plowed her with Prozac in combination with some sort of stimulant. I wondered how Miss Kelly got her drugs in. I was shocked that creatures like Miss Kelly survived in the daylight and that she was even astir. Where was her casket?

The box was opened and rifled though. "What is this, customs?" I said. I tried to remember what was on the list. Let me see, there was coconut hair pomade for Trina, earrings, lipstick for Camilla, Girl Scout cookies for Ruth, wax for Lucia. What else was in there? I couldn't remember for the life of me.

*   *   *

USA VS MINA SALLON — DETROIT, MI — APRIL 2007 — 5:26 PM
She said, "The other red flag was the equipment list. Sami Al-Mufti sent an

equipment list to Sallon, which Sami distinctly said was for a project in Iraq. Another red flag was that Sami Al-Mufti sent shipping documents stating that the equipment was sent November 18th, 2003. And there was also an installation certificate that was dated November 2nd, 2003. The equipment is installed in Turkey before it's even shipped? Does that make any sense? That's a red flag."

Yes, it did make sense. I worked with Sami on the oil-for-food program and the equipment list *she* was talking about wasn't the same GSM telecommunications equipment destined for Turkey. The prosecution was making the argument that, since I was involved in this program, I may have been involved with Iraq in other capacities.

Nonetheless, was it a red flag that Sami provided an installation certificate that was dated before the shipping documents for Turkey? Absolutely. So why didn't she call him to the stand?

*   *   *

"What do you want for it?" Miss B said. "Our shit." Was it a red flag that Miss Kelly stole our drop? Absolutely. She read aloud a letter addressed to me:

> *Mina, I couldn't get the cigarettes, there just wasn't enough time on my end to run around to all of these different places, honey. – Love, Mom*

My mom was a horrible criminal, to say the least.

Miss Kelly tucked the note into her pants. "Does your mom like green, Sallon? When I call on you, you'll come."

"I'm not going to a second location with you." Miss B said. Miss Kelly shoved the box at her.

Chapter 9:

Venomous Spiders

When Miss B and I received Miss Kelly's dinner summons, we second-guessed why we were invited. She sent out hand-made invitations. They were black and white. Classic. Miss Kelly probably paid one of her cronies to write out our names in cursive. Miss B's name was spelled wrong. The "Miss" was missing. She was pretty peeved about that.

Still, we wondered, why pull out all the stops for a social gathering? The time of arrival was set an hour before the last count: 8 p.m. sharp on a Friday. Seemed like a Last Supper type of event. Or was it a sing for your supper soiree? Was it some kind of truce? A stimulus? The location was spooky: Devil's Den.

*   *   *

It was my last year in prison, although I didn't know it at the time. I didn't pay attention to the things that usually forged happiness in people: family, hot weather and letters. People (by people, I mean very few) now tended to send letters that made my situation "look better." They also sent letters that were brutally honest.

February 14, 2012: *At 87, my mother is in a dependent care facility and has gotten to the point where she cannot dress herself, figure out how to put her glasses on, or answer the phone without it being upside down. It's very hard to see her forget the word for "feet" or "tv." Everything is now "that thing." She isn't herself. Please don't forget yourself. No one wants a knock off! There is only one you, don't lose yourself! – Isabel Baker*

February 16, 2012: *Boy, I would have never thought my life would consist of anti-depressants to get through the day, caffeine to keep me going, and sleeping pills to get me to sleep. And, because I don't move very much, I have gained weight. Now, that's not good. My knees are good. But I have really screwed up my right foot. The pain is unbearable. Not sure what I did, but after checking how much insurance will cover, I decided I have to see a foot doctor. And when you come home (no ... I don't have a specific time) we can go somewhere. Just a little time with you, that would be great.*

Every time the phone rings I think it's a collection call. I just let it go to voicemail. My credit sucks and I don't even care. You would say "shame on ya" if you saw how I lived now. Don't do much around the house... tend to throw my clothes in a pile in the bedroom with a path to the bed. I love paper plates! I'm getting really fond of plastic silverware, too! Poor Micah calls sometimes and asks if I'm alive in there. The dog seems to understand a lot when I talk to her, ha! And she always checks for cuts and bruises to lick.

Well, best put this to rest. Mina, please try to be patient. I think of all the people you dealt with and how they all disappeared so fast... no calls. There are few, very few. We may not have much, but we do have each other. Keep the faith, please believe, and have patience—I have to! – All my love, mom

February 18, 2012: *Mina, everyone in the community told me it was in my best interest not to write about your case. If you recall, it took me a while to commit fully. But, after many talks with my husband and much prayer, I took on the risk, with no pay, reimbursement, or business assurances of any kind. At the time I didn't share these discomforts with you (that still linger in me) because I figure you're in such a bad state as it is. The last thing you need is another person turning their back on you.*

As you know, there are a lot of challenges in telling this story. Justifying your character is difficult and will make readers unsympathetic towards you. Also, many publishers won't find your story compelling. So, if you still want me to be a part of it your name needs to be exonerated.

There are millions of people who are victimized around the world, the majority of whom haven't had the chance to get their story told. I apologize that up until this point all I have had to offer you is a free telling of your story and a little advocacy (though you may think it has not helped but no one else's painstaking efforts have either). Please feel free to share this information with your family as you find appropriate. – Abida

*   *   *

On Friday, we made our way to Devil's Den. Not many people had the gall to enter the room. Maybe that was why the event was held in Devil's Den. The place was, more often than not, empty. We wouldn't be bothered. It was the type of invitation where one's insides screamed "NO." Where one's heart pumped blood a little faster. Where one's lungs breathed air a little harder. And where one's bladder seemed infinitely smaller. But we went through with the plight anyway. Why? Miss B and I didn't want to deal with the consequences had we not attended.

I poked my head in the triangular windows before we went in. There was a shitty quality of light, but it wasn't dim. Dingy maybe? Yes, dingy was the word.

"The disciples are gathering," Miss B said. "Don't be shaky." I guess I was fidgeting. She always said that when I was a tad nervous. "Don't be shaky."

As we entered, there were four dark human shapes already there: Miss Kelly, Blaze and two other girls, Miss Kelly's subordinates. Miss Kelly extended her bony arm and passed around plates. They sat on the floor in a circle.

Chicken and rice were on the menu. They hadn't started eating. They weren't even conversing. Just sort of sitting there. Were they praying? Were they facing the four corners like "The Craft?" Why the fuck were they just sitting there?

The room looked like someone intended to renovate it but fell short. The innards of the walls were exposed: fiberglass and mold. I itched just looking at it.

"Welcome," Miss Kelly said, patting the floor with her long fingers.

"What is this?" Miss B said, "BYOC: Bring your own chair?"

As I sat down, I saw what seemed to be scratch marks on the walls, or maybe the rumors about Devil's Den were clawing at my head. Either way, the marks exposed the room's former color, orange. A burnt type of orange, the hue of late fall, of decaying leaves, of brain fungus on dead wood, of poison ivy rust.

I followed the scratch marks up the wall to the ceiling. It was also cracking. Looked like water damage. If there was a theme to the room, water damage was it. I thought that the hosing down of the insane patients years ago could have caused the water wounds. Ice baths, complete with psychotic water splatter, also could have done in the room.

Blaze looked sickly. She was pale and shivered. The room was warm; too warm. I couldn't imagine why she was cold. Was she sick? Withdrawals? She passed Miss B a plate with an unsteady hand. Miss B politely declined.

"Just ate baby but thank you."

"In some countries, declining food is a great offense," Miss Kelly said.

I grabbed the plate and shoveled some rice into my mouth.

"Compliments to the chef," I said.

Blaze's head dropped and she looked very disoriented. She pounded the ground repeatedly: boom, boom, boom. She focused on a separate area of the room, entranced. Maybe it was a closet some time ago, but there wasn't a door. It was just an unclean and hollowed out hole in the wall. Boom, boom, boom.

Miss Kelly moved her head, blocking Blaze. She raised a cup.

"To new beginnings," she said.

I raised my plate and took a bite of chicken. It was good for what it was.

"Why we here?" Miss B said, cutting through the shit. You could always count on her for that. Cutting to the chase.

I cocked my head and studied a stain on the wall. It looked like an upside-down ogre with sharp teeth. Or maybe it was a bulbous demonic cauliflower head. Miss B grabbed my hand because I was probably fidgeting again.

"It's a friendly gathering," Miss Kelly said, "Nothing more."

"Everyone is working an angle," Miss B said.

I didn't like the look of the triangular windows. They were murky and medicinal. The thought of past patients locked in this very room sent shivers down my spine. I thought of them creeping around and peeping out of those angular windows. I also wondered what the patients were committed for. Homosexuality? Mania? Melancholia? Was it "shocked" out of them?

"Now that you mention it, I'd like a hit on my son-in-law," said Miss Kelly in a way that seemed halfway like a joke.

"And how we gunna do that?" Miss B said.

"You two are resourceful. Figure it out. You know I still have it. The letter."

"We'll get right on it," Miss B said.

"See this as a warning."

"Excuse me?" Miss B said. "What's the warning?"

The stain looked like it was now upright. And the ogre's hair was curled. What the fuck? Was it some sort of optical horror? I was tired. I must have been tired. I was tired. Right?

I wondered if I could fit into the separate area. I could have curled up and seeped into the wall with the fiberglass and lead pipes. Then I'd be gone.

"Let's go," Miss B said.

But I couldn't. I wanted to lie down. I wanted to sleep. I could nap, I thought. Blaze was out cold. The voices vanished into the wall.

I didn't trust myself in this room anymore. It was like drinking too much in an unknown place. The feeling of flying with a fear of heights. I tried to stand up, but I think I was on my knees. Yes, I must have been on my knees.

I reached for the demon. I thought that if I touched it, it would be okay. I just needed to touch it. Could I touch it? It would leave if I touched it.

The last thing I remembered seeing was that ugly demon's face.

*   *   *

I found myself face down in a toilet bowl as Miss B held my hair. Puke was everywhere: splashed on the toilet bowl, on the floor and on the wall. I couldn't stop coughing. Chunks of rice flew out of my mouth. Then came the yellow stuff; was it called bile?

"I can't breathe. I can't breathe," I gasped.

"You are whiter than usual," Miss B said.

I attempted to stand, wavered and fell right into a rusted piece of metal, gashing open my leg. The last thing I recall seeing was the blood.

*   *   *

Blood trickled along the floor as we staggered down the hallway. The hallway had cots and cons lining it. This hallway was known as *The Green Mile*. It was where the worst cons slept. The lights were on 24/7 and nothing was hidden. People stared but all were silenced. My eyes couldn't focus properly.

Miss B kept pausing to get a better grip on my failing body. It was limp and sweaty. She kept saying things like "You're going to be okay," and "Just breathe, baby."

She held me up against the wall to reposition her grip. No one helped.

My throat burned so badly that I thought it was corroded. I kept touching the outside to make sure that a hole hadn't formed.

"What you doing, baby?"

I couldn't talk. I couldn't walk. I couldn't see. My vision was now doubled. Maybe it was tripled. Quadrupled? It was a whole lot of fucked up.

The lights were off in Medical and it was locked. It closed around 8:30 p.m.

"Jesus Christ!" Miss B yelled. She told me later that I started to convulse when she ran for help. I vaguely recall seeing her shoes as I drifted onto my side. The spotless shoes she had purchased for herself. She was so proud that she was able to do that: treat herself. For a time, I wondered it this would be the last time I'd see Miss B. Would this be the last time I lay down? Would this be the last time I breathed?

*   *   *

Was I in medical for a few hours, a few days or a few weeks? I didn't know. Having MRSA was like being expunged. My whole body went into shock. I thanked the rusty metal in the bathroom for that and I added it to my wide-ranging catalog of sicknesses.

Mr. Clark had opened Medical and called the doctor in. He didn't have to do that. But had he not, I would have died. That was the prognosis.

One day, I opened my eyes.

"There she is! What up, Detroit?" I stared at Miss B and cried. I think I was confused. My throat was so scratchy. It hurt to breathe.

"Can you hear me?" I could hear her. A doctor checked my vitals and silently filled out a chart. She also consulted with Mr. Clark.

Miss B and I stared at the doctor. We both wanted her to turn around, to turn around and say that I'd be okay. I tried to raise my head.

"Try not to move too much, okay?" she said to me, finally. I nodded.

"Do you know your name?"

I nodded. "Detroit," with a hoarse voice. Miss B laughed.

The doctor flashed a pen light in my eyes.

"Apart from the MRSA, you have mild burns in your esophagus. Typically, this is the result of poison."

"Jesus," Miss B said. "Did you hear that, Mr. Clark? Poison."

I said, "Maybe they'll get transferred."

"It going to take more than that to make these fuckers drop like flies, Detroit."

Mr. Clark said, "You got a friend 'till the end," before he left the room. After I was poisoned, Mr. Clark told me that he "stopped seeing inmates and started seeing people that had made mistakes."

I turned to Miss B. "Why am I here?" I couldn't stop crying.

"You were poisoned, baby."

"Why am I here in this prison?"

"Sallon, you're here for me," she said. "I kept praying to God that one day I'd be able to see. Now I do. You made me believe in myself, Sallon."

A few days later, Blaze informed me, as she lowered her voice, that Miss Kelly had dumped bleach into the rice. Rice that had been intended for Miss B.

"Why would she attack Miss B?"

"She wants her out of the way," Blaze said.

She wanted her out of the way so that she could get to me.

Bureau of Prisons Health Services, 2011	Inmate Name: **Mary, Mina** Description	Reg # 30810-039 Type
Health Problem 9/1/11	ADHD *we do not medicate	Chronic
Health Problem 9/1/11	Common migraine	Chronic
Health Problem 9/1/11	Chronic Pain Syndrome	Current
Health Problem 9/1/11	Shoulder Pain	Acute
Health Problem 9/1/11	Dyspepsia (stomach pain)	Current
Health Problem 9/1/11	Pharyngitis	Acute
Health Problem 9/1/11	Allergic Rhinitis	Current
Health Problem 9/1/11	Esophageal reflux	Current
Health Problem 9/1/11	MRSA- right leg	Current

*   *   *

Miss B met with my father and Micah when I was incapacitated. Miss B relayed the visitation for me. She said that they arrived early and were eagerly awaiting my arrival. They expected that I'd rise from the dead. She related that I was out of action.

"I'm out of action, too," my father said. He had flown in from Iraq when he heard that I had been poisoned. The General would have to wait.

"Thank you for being her friend," Micah said.

"Fam recognizes fam," Miss B said. "She's my family."

"Then so are we," my father said.

They were her first visitors and she said they made her feel like family. They laughed, they broke bread, and they spoke without boundaries.

"How are you doing, Micah?" Miss B said.

"No one has ever asked me that before."

"Well, someone ought to."

"Tell her I'm not going anywhere," my father said.

*   *   *

USA VS MINA SALLON — DETROIT, MI — APRIL 2007 — 5:30 PM

She said, "This is a deal that caused Curve Tech revenues to soar from $700,000 in 2002 to over $5 million in 2003. $41,000 was Mansur Sallon's cut out of the Curve Tech bank account. That was the father's cut from this deal. Sallon gave her father a cut because he brought in the deal."

My father felt responsible in a way that no father should. Sami was introduced to him through a distant cousin. And family friends were generally trusted.

*   *   *

"I'll take care of her," Miss B said. My father and Micah shook hands with her and swore they'd meet again (on the outside).

*   *   *

Miss B knew Miss Kelly would be in the laundry room on Saturday at 3 p.m. She had been keeping track of her movements for five years. She was waiting with a vengeance and a bag of oranges that she had bought from Camilla.

"This better be good," Miss Kelly said.

The Black troupe emerged from hiding as the dryers spun. Miss B had bribed them with food and the bag of oranges, but it was well worth it.

The Mexican clique left the laundry room out of respect for Miss B. Plus, they couldn't be witnesses if they hadn't seen anything. And they didn't.

Miss B slung the orange bag at Miss Kelly's face with the force of all of Florida. KO, while the troupe attended to Miss Kelly's pets. It was a short fight and Miss Kelly sure as hell didn't see it coming.

Miss B didn't see her transfer coming, either. Mr. Clark pulled her into his office and related that they'd be shipping her behind the fence. He said, "There is nothing I can do about it." He claimed he knew that she beat the crap out of Miss Kelly and that the guards were privy to her receiving money (via

Western Union from Detroit). But they got her on contraband: the 20 pairs of shoes under her bed. The shock of it all left us speechless. In fact, we were too chock-full of surprise for goodbyes.

We were too choked-up for goodbyes, too.

Miss B told me at a later date that the corrections officers (cough, cough, Rachel) did offer her a plea bargain if she gave them my head on a spit. The girl didn't budge. She didn't even think about it. She was the most loyal friend that I have ever had, and I had to go to prison to find her.

She wrote me a letter from behind the fence and it was all I had heard from her. I imagined that she was a little bit lost, a little bit angered, and a little bit depressed.

They ain't tell me where I was goin' when I hopped over. Grab yo shit, they said. Mr. Clark said there was nothin' he could have done. They got me on those stinky ass shoes, Detroit! But boy ain't oranges good. Ride or Die, baby!

Behind the fence be shady, so shady my piss is black! Detroit, stay out!

It was just like Miss B to joke about kidney cancer. Behind the fence be so shady, my urine is black. She has been complaining about pain in her side for as long as I could remember. A formidable silence struck me when I read her letter. How could I help her behind the fence, especially in the position I was in now?

Miss Kelly gave Mr. Clark my mom's letter as proof of evidence that we had been shipping contraband to Kentucky. She had swiped another letter from by bunk (a sample of mom's handwriting) and tried to serve him with the argument that it came from the same person. What was she, a handwriting analyst?

The business was over. No more dealings were to be made.

Chapter 10

No More Visitors

I was shipped to *The Green Mile* with the bad cons and the 24/7 fluorescents. The prison was overpopulated, and passageways were suddenly called bedrooms or "living spaces." Our hallway had the odd aroma pairing of bleach and a soup kitchen. Nauseating. Inmates tramped past my poor excuse for a bed as they made their way to the mess hall, and then trudged back through my bedroom leaving their crumbs behind.

My surroundings spun with the inmates until around the second week I was there. Vertigo. 24/7 lights didn't help the cluster fuck and the clobber of my headache. The only time I felt good was when my eyes were closed.

When I got up to eat or use the restroom (which were the only times I got up), I felt like a blind person in a Ford, navigating through Michigan's crappy roads. I hit pothole after pothole. Some were the size of graves.

One night in December, Blaze died. They discovered her in Miss Kelly's room, stone cold and in a fetal position. She had passed away in the night and went unnoticed until morning.

She went unnoticed until morning.

Cons whispered about her death like it was a hot topic.

"She couldn't take the time," Trina said.

"I heard Miss Kelly done it," said Elderberry, "feeding her all them pills like candy."

I couldn't stop thinking about how lucky Blaze was. She didn't have deal with whatever prison threw her way anymore. She was free and at peace. I also couldn't stop thinking about how she had just smiled at me in the hallway. How she had just asked me if I could put money on her account to call her kid. How she had recently crafted a card for me with flowers on it. The card said, "Never too busy to stop and say hello."

I kept replaying our conversation that day and every day for a while. I remembered her playful laugh and her buttery comments like, "Faith moves mountains," or, "When the going gets tough, the tough get going."

My dad passed about four years after I was released. I was supposed to meet him for lunch at his favorite place. He was late and then he never showed up. When I called him, he said he'd have to reschedule because he was admitted into the hospital for "a minor thing." He said that I shouldn't worry, as most caring parents did when shit hit the fan. Friends also told me not to worry, as good friends did. I knew different.

Soon, the left side of his face went numb and his sentences were sparse, although he was still sharp as a tack. One day I saw him lying in his hospital bed hooked up to stuff that was keeping him alive. He smiled crookedly, as if he knew something I didn't. He said in a slur of words, "Make sure you write your book. And make a movie, too!" One day he didn't speak at all.

And soon after, he was lying in a wooden casket. Next to him were photographs of him in his prime. My favorite was the one showcasing his plump cheeks, warm smile and a gigantic purple turnip in his hand. That picture made me laugh. It was the one I pulled up when I bragged about him. I told people about how he helped release 10,000 people in an Iraqi prison camp. Although he was firm, he went to bat for his family and never lost. Well, almost never. The only person he couldn't free was me.

He liked to make things grow. His garden in Metamora was proof of that. Maybe that's what I like about the photograph with the stupid turnip. It reminded me that he made a difference in so many lives. I wanted to be like him.

I didn't know how to honor him when his wife asked me what my wishes were for his funeral. Truth is, I thought the turnip would make him laugh. He was serious when it came to business, but laughter was always on the table.

In front of his casket was a folded red prayer kneeler. Christians, Muslims and agnostics kneeled to send him to heaven. That was another thing I loved about him. He brought people together. I knew he was there, in heaven. So did his wife. So did his girlfriend. No one was perfect. But the good outweighed the bad. I think that means something to God. If he were at the funeral, he probably would have turned to me and said something like, "Look how open minded I've become, Mina."

As I curled up in my very public bunk along *The Green Mile*, I thought a lot about death. How some people slipped into it via pills or an overdose. And how others were shot with it, via a Colt 22lr. Or, some people, like Saddam, hung in the air until their voice box collapsed.

I was cut off from everything that had mattered to me. The warmth of anything familiar was pulled away with the summer months. My family hadn't visited since June, Miss B was long gone, and food didn't carry the same weight as it did. I got to feeling that I couldn't move.

Around this time, my mom had a stroke. I asked my brother exactly what had happened. He said that she had finally gotten around to cleaning out my car (in the dead of winter) and she collapsed. That was that.

I had discovered later on that she had literally plunged into my passenger seat, trash bag in hand. She didn't want to let go of my stuff. She called him when her face was frozen. (The numbness in her left arm wasn't enough of an emergency.) He knew something was wrong when she said something like, "Call Micah, my, my, call." She related after I was released that, in the previous year, her drive was gone. She couldn't take it. Neither could I.

Micah said that my mom's house was falling apart around her. The front entrance looked about 200 years old. The snow and ice continued to thaw and enter the front door at the floor level. It caused an ongoing mess every time water was involved. She paid good money to have a new door installed but nothing changed. Leaks were still widespread. The ceiling in the living room wasn't any different. Micah said on numerous occasions, he'd enter the house to find mom watching the rain leak in. She settled on observing the damage as it set in. She didn't have the energy to fix things. My brother said that she wouldn't be visiting anymore.

She wouldn't be visiting anymore.

But I had other visitors. Miss Kelly popped a squat on my cot. She squeezed my swollen leg. She liked to inch in on the vulnerable like a spider would. A fly flailed in her orb and she waited in the wings, so to speak, until it couldn't move.

"She beat me with oranges," she said.

I looked up from my wheel of wooziness, "Did you expect something sweeter?"

"It's going to be a long road."

"You mean I can't just click my heels and go home?"

Miss Kelly looked around. The second rotation of cons entered the mess hall as the early dinner cons (the special needs people and the elderly) left. Her eyes shot at me in a deadly stillness.

"The only way out of here is death. I can get you something if you need it." She released her grip on my leg and patted it. "A razor, a rope, some pills. You decide. The only thing I'll need are three letters. One for the prison, one for your mother, and one for me." With that, she ripped three sheets of paper out of a journal and handed them to me. I took them.

Ten or so watches beeped. I rolled into a standing position and stood in front of my bed. It was the 4 p.m. count. Rachel stormed into the space all high and mighty.

"One, two, three and thief." She pointed the counter at me when she said "thief," as if it would blow me to smithereens.

Someone once told me that when people went to prison, getting out would be the most difficult thing they'd have to do. They were right.

*   *   *

I tried to write my mom a letter. One that would explain why I needed to go. After her birthday was the right timing. No, after Christmas was the right timing. It might kill her if it happened before Christmas, I thought. It wasn't too late to do it after Christmas. No, it wasn't too late. I had hoped that she would read the letter and understand. That she would sigh a breath of relief knowing that she wouldn't have to work so hard trying to get me released anymore. All I could come up with was—*Mom, I can't do it anymore.*

Mom, I can't do it anymore.

At the same time, my mom was writing her own letter, which I came across a couple years after I was home. It said:

> *I long for her freedom. Simple freedom. Mina has already served her time. I have really come to hate my country. How long will it take for Americans to wake up, to see their rights disappearing before their eyes? I am tired. Heaven seems so much better than this right now. Should I stay or should I go?*

"Should I stay, or should I go?"

I thought about Saddam's hanging on December 30, 2006. Supposedly, he refused to wear the black hood that concealed his face. I thought about him dangling as the platform fell beneath his feet. I thought about the words he voiced before he died. "Don't be afraid," he said.

Don't be afraid.

I thought about how most Iraqis celebrated. It was the end of a dictator, a tyrant and a terrorist! I was definitely celebrating that day.

I thought about George W. Bush's March 2003 promise as he formally launched Operation Iraqi Freedom. "My fellow citizens, the dangers to our country and the world will be overcome. We will pass through this time of peril and carry on the work of peace. We will defend our freedom. We will bring freedom to others and we will prevail."

I thought about how *She* was sworn in as U.S. attorney for the Eastern District of Michigan on the heels of my case. I imagined that federal judges, members of Congress and the bar were all happy to be witnessing the act. I imagined that her right hand would have been raised as a chief judge swore her in. I imagined her words, "I will support and defend the constitution of the United States against all enemies, foreign and domestic."

I thought about how they pinned me as a domestic enemy.

I thought about how President Barak Obama addressed the nation on October 21, 2011, as America pulled out from the war in Iraq. He said, "… I can report that, as promised, the rest of our troops in Iraq will come home by the end of the year. After nearly nine years, America's war in Iraq will be over. Over the next two months, our troops in Iraq – tens of thousands of them – will pack up their gear and board convoys for the journey home."

I wrote Miss Kelly a letter and dropped it on her bunk.

Not today, Satan.

*   *   *

Micah promised that when I was released, he'd fly to Kentucky in his airplane and zoom me out of there. The warden said, "That won't fly."

It was the last time that I visited Mr. Clark's office.

"I have your date," Mr. Clark said.

"When?"

"Three months. Out for good behavior. 2012 is your year."

"Thank you so much," I said.

"You don't belong here," he said. "Took me a whole lot to figure it out, but Mina Sallon, you do not belong here. Go live your life."

He nudged the Kleenex box my way.

"Do you think we can make it two months?" I finally asked when I could talk again. We laughed.

"I'm going to say this one more time, Sallon. Mind your damn business. Don't disrespect anybody. Do your time. Don't feed the animals."

*   *   *

She came marching back like she owned the place, among cat calls and whistles. She carried hygiene items and that god-awful, itchy bedroll. I was so happy to see her.

"Here comes trouble," Miss B said. She looked me over. "What hit you, a bus or something?"

*   *   *

I was back in the bus stop with Miss B. The last 30 days were so long. We were both on the straight and narrow. There were a lot of "I'm not getting out of bed" days. Not because we were depressed, but because we were anxious. We didn't want to fuck it up. She was also getting out in 18 months. We had great plans.

"The first thing I'm going to do is eat a steak," I said.

"I'm coming to see you," Miss B said, popping jellybeans into her mouth.

The highlight of Miss B's life was in prison and it was hard for me to fathom that. She once told me that it was the most comfortable she had ever been.

"You can't cross state lines," I said.

She waved me away, "I didn't read that nowhere."

We both laughed. We knew the story after prison all too well. We'd both be living in halfway houses for about a year, and then onto house arrest. We wouldn't be allowed to cross state lines. We would have to be on our best behavior and remain sober. It would be difficult to get a job because reputable companies did not hire felons. (I was turned down by McDonalds). We'd be receiving help from the government in the form of supplemental income, but it wouldn't be enough to survive.

"Don't tell no one your date," Miss B said.

*   *   *

Two weeks before my release date, there was a drop that would have put Pablo Escobar to shame. There was cocaine, blunts, Xanax and alcohol … a dizzying minefield of infractions. That year, 2012, was a lucky year because a lot of cons were getting released for "good behavior."

Any guess as to who organized the drop?

"Help yourself, ladies," Miss Kelly's voice sounded self-important as she paraded through the library with her treasure trove of narcotics and a red cup in hand, presumably filled with alcohol. She seemed to be quite pleased with herself for not only orchestrating the drop but that she could also get away with it.

"Whatchu got?" Miss B asked. I grabbed her arm. She pulled away and dug through the box.

"There's some crack in there somewhere," Miss Kelly said. This was a low blow. The war on drugs, initiated by Nixon and enhanced by Reagan, cracked down on African Americans by serving harsher sentences for individuals caught with crack, which was a cheaper alternative to cocaine. Most were Black people. There were lighter sentences for those caught with cocaine. Mostly white people. So, around 1986, five grams of crack equaled a five-year minimum sentence in prison, while 500 grams of cocaine also equaled a five-year minimum sentence. However, crack and cocaine were essentially the same drug in different forms. How did this make sense? This war contributed to the mass incarceration of Black people.

"Because I'm black, I do crack?" Miss B said as she pulled a bag out of Miss Kelly's box that looked like methamphetamine crystal.

"Thanks, baby," she continued. "People talk a lot of shit about you, but you're okay in my books." Miss B raised her Bible. She grabbed some vodka. "This is for her," she said.

Miss Kelly served Miss B an absentminded smile and did a loop around the library, handing out her supply.

"You can't be that stupid," I said.
"This is for Blaze."

*   *   *

We followed Miss Kelly around for a good part of the day, waiting for her to slip. She didn't. It helped that she had all of the guards wrapped around her finger, until she set that red cup down in her room. She took a regular afternoon nap around 2 p.m. and her regular watchdogs appeared to be off duty. They were no doubt off boozing it up somewhere.

Miss B took a sip. "Bitch is drinking water," she whispered.

In one little sleight-of-hand the methamphetamine made its way into her drink and into her eventual mouth when she woke up parched.

About two hours later, after counts, the guards made the cons take either breathalyzers or urine tests at random. Rachel used a breathalyzer on me. Of course, she did.

Miss Kelly was instructed to piss in a cup, as was Miss B. Miss B said that Miss Kelly exited the restroom with such confidence. It didn't last long.

She was sent behind the fence to some maximum-security prison in Georgia. And she was launched there with the same drug that she fed Blaze with, the drug that caused her eventual death, as her toxicology report detected. Miss B was a poet. It was very Shakespearean.

*   *   *

I was released in the spring of 2012. Mr. Clark and Miss B were there when I was processed out. In all honesty, I never thought that two African Americans would be my greatest friends and best advocates in prison. But there they were.

It was a bittersweet moment. Sweet because the birds were chirping, and I'd soon be free. Bitter because I was leaving my new flock.

"Detroit's finest," Miss B said.

"I never would have survived in this place without you," I told her.

"And I would have been hungry as shit," Miss B said.

"A friend till the end." We linked and locked pinkie fingers.

I turned to Mr. Clark. "I'm going to miss our conversations. But mostly the air conditioning."

"I'm not going to wish you luck. You don't need it," Mr. Clark said. "Get out."

"Can I hug you?" I asked.

"You can do what you want," he said, "You're no longer my problem."

We hugged. And I actually saw tears. I handed him a $200 gift card. "For your kids," I said.

He looked at the gift card and smiled. "You are something else, Sallon," he said. "A good something else."

*   *   *

I never thought that I'd stretch my arms, walk out of a door and breathe fresh air again.

The soft country breeze at my late father's 65-acre farmhouse, in Metamora, seemed so far away. So distant when he made the drive to federal with me four years earlier.

My mother said that his buying up all that land was my father's way of trying to reach a state of simplicity in his later years. "Your father aimed to recreate what brought him peace in his childhood. He grew up with little, but was happy, nonetheless. Gardening, raising birds and cutting the land. People did that on the cusp of retirement; they recreated the good days, the simple days."

To be honest, even the air conditioning at Whole Foods (blasting in my face) seemed fresh after so much time behind ironclad locks.

The simple days came after prison. I shopped at the Salvation Army and dated a farmer, someone who also cut the land. When people asked why I wasn't married and didn't have children (at the age of 40), I told them it was because I had been through a decade of hell.

For years, I ached to breathe in anything that didn't have that Kentucky smell of fried chicken, manure and toasted peanuts. I did not write this book to roast Kentucky. While I was locked up, I heard that the Kentucky people (on the outside) were beyond friendly, that the bourbon and bluegrass were stellar, and that the city was pristine beyond measure. However, prison in Lexington was a different beast.

Miss B was released 18 months later. I saw her from time to time, when she used her daughter's ID to cross state lines. Her kidney cancer metastasized but with harrowing treatment, she beat it. Thank God.

Miss Kelly died from cardiac arrest about six months after she was finally released.

After Sami Al-Mufti finally answered my call and I spoke with him, he said, "The whole thing was for freedom and they took away yours." No shit, pal.

I didn't get enough time with my father before he passed away. But I would honor his request. "Make sure you write your book. And make a movie, too!"

My mother struggled with her health and our decade of defeat dashed many of her dreams, including the dream to travel the world. Her body imprisoned her.

Micah resumed teaching and sold his company. He retired at the tender age of 40. He still flies a plane, which I never understood until now. He does it to feel free. My sentence held my entire family captive.

Micah still flies to feel free.

I still had to survive a halfway house, but that's another story…

Bureau of Prisons Health Services, 2011	**Inmate Name:** **Mary, Mina** Description	**Reg # 30810-039** Type
Health Problem 3/20/12	ADHD *we do not medicate	Chronic
Health Problem 3/20/12	Common migraine	Chronic
Health Problem 3/20/12	Chronic Pain Syndrome	Current
Health Problem 3/20/12	Shoulder Pain	Acute
Health Problem 3/20/12	Dyspepsia (stomach pain)	Current
Health Problem 3/20/12	Pharyngitis	Acute
Health Problem 3/20/12	Allergic Rhinitis	Current
Health Problem 3/20/12	Esophageal reflux	Current
Health Problem 3/20/12	MRSA- right leg	Current
Health Problem 3/20/12	Ankle Burn	Current
Health Problem 3/20/12	Candidiasis of vulva	Current
Health Problem 3/20/12	Otitis Media	Current